GUERCINO IN BRITAIN

Paintings from British Collections

Introductory essays by Michael Helston and Francis Russell

Catalogue by Michael Helston and Tom Henry
based on the researches of
Denis Mahon

Published by National Gallery Publications Limited, London
and The Burlington Magazine Publications Ltd

Exhibition dates
The National Gallery, London
28th June – 31st July 1991

This catalogue is published by The Burlington Magazine Publications Ltd, 6 Bloomsbury Square, London WC1A 2LP, and by National Gallery Publications Limited, 5/6 Pall Mall East, London SW1Y 5BA.
It is also published as a supplement to The Burlington Magazine, Vol.CXXXIII, no.1060, July 1991.

British Library Cataloguing in Publication Data
Guercino, 1591-1666
Guercino in Britain
I. Title II. Helston, Michael III. Mahon, Denis
741, 945
ISBN 0-947645-98-5
Library of Congress Catalog Card Number 91-061340

Designed and edited by The Burlington Magazine

Typeset and printed in Great Britain by Jolly & Barber Ltd, Rugby

Contents

Foreword

It may at first seem odd that London should be celebrating so energetically the fourth centenary of Guercino's birth, with exhibitions at both the British Museum and the National Gallery. After all, Guercino himself categorically refused to visit this country, on the linked grounds of our Protestantism and our weather; while Britain, having collected from France and Italy a startling number of his finest paintings, subsequently allowed most of them to leave again in the direction of the United States.

Yet whatever coolness or carelessness may have existed in the recent past, two compelling reasons explain our present admiration and enjoyment of his work. The first is the presence in the Royal Collection of one of the greatest holdings of Guercino drawings, catalogued only in 1989, but an inspiration to artists for over two centuries. The second is Sir Denis Mahon. For nearly sixty years Sir Denis has championed the cause of Italian seventeenth-century painting in general and of Guercino in particular. His were the publications that re-opened eyes closed by the eloquent prejudices of Ruskin. His was the verve that did so much for the success of the pioneering exhibitions of Bolognese painting in the 1950s and 1960s. And it is to his generosity that we are all indebted for the promise that most of his collection of the great Bolognese and other Italian masters of the seventeenth century will, after his death, be distributed among British public galleries.

This small show at the National Gallery is a – perhaps opportunistic – prelude to the much larger exhibition of paintings which will be held this autumn in Bologna: we decided to gather as many as possible of the paintings by Guercino now in Britain so that they might be seen by the London public before collectively taking wing for Italy. With signal generosity, owners have agreed to part with their pictures for even longer than they had at first expected. An exhibition of the artist's drawings from British Collections runs at the British Museum to 18th August, and we hope that his quatercentenary may thus be enjoyed as fully in this country, which once so enthusiastically admired and collected him, as in Bologna itself. Catalogue entries for other paintings by Guercino in British collections, not lent for the exhibition, have been included in the interests of completeness.

As the opening of the Sainsbury Wing approaches, the mounting of even so modest an exhibition has placed many extra burdens on colleagues at the National Gallery, and a special debt of gratitude is owned to Michael Helston, Herb Gilman, Margaret Stewart and Michael Wilson. We could not have embarked on this venture, far less brought it to fulfilment, without the support of Sir Denis Mahon, the whole-hearted co-operation of The Burlington Magazine (in particular of Duncan Bull), the scholarly contributions of Francis Russell and Tom Henry, and the generous help of an anonymous benefactor. To them all, and to the owners of the paintings, on behalf of everyone at the National Gallery, I should like to express our warmest thanks.

NEIL MACGREGOR
Director

MICHAEL HELSTON

An outline of Guercino's life

Guercino's career is remarkable in several ways. His life and work are comparatively well documented, and the histories of large numbers of his paintings can be traced to their actual commissions. There are three prime reasons why this is so. Though his first biographer, Count Carlo Cesare Malvasia (1616-1693) knew him personally, Guercino himself was rather reticent; after the master's death, Malvasia was, however, given access to documentation in his house. Guercino's meticulously kept account book (the *Libro dei Conti*) is fortunately preserved, giving details of commissions, prices for paintings and their dates from 1629 until 1666, the year of his death at the age of 75. There is also a large amount of correspondence which corroborates much of the information in these sources and provides a good deal more.[1]

Although Guercino quickly established an international reputation as one of the finest painters in Italy, being courted by the kings of England and France, he chose, for most of his life, to remain largely in his native town of Cento, moving permanently to nearby Bologna by 1644. Partly because of this apparent unwillingness to travel, his life – especially the later part of it – was relatively uneventful in many respects, and this is one of the reasons why accounts tend to concentrate on the earlier years.

Guercino seems, to a large extent, to have been self-taught. During the period when we might expect him to have been serving an apprenticeship his name was connected with three very minor local painters; but by 1612, when he was twenty-one, he had come to the attention of a Bolognese cleric, the Canonico Antonio Mirandola, who held an ecclesiastical position at Cento and secured Guercino some important commissions as an artist in his own right. In this way he came to the notice of other, more important, patrons and collectors, principally Bolognese, and his reputation was assured from early in his career. Unfortunately many of the works from this earliest period remain unknown or have been lost.

Born in Cento in 1591 he was baptised Giovanni Francesco Barbieri on 8th February. The nickname Guercino, by which he has always been known, derives from the fact that he had a squint, discernible in the self-portrait illustrated here (Fig.1). It is probable that the young Guercino visited Bologna on several occasions: it is the nearest large city to Cento and a natural centre of gravity for the Centese, even though Cento itself belonged to the Papal territory of Ferrara. Indeed one of the minor painters the young Guercino seems to have worked with, Paolo Zagnoni, was based in Bologna. The main importance of this for Guercino would have been the opportunity to see paintings by several leading artists, especially those of the Carracci family and their circle. He was also familiar with Ferrara, the next largest city in the vicinity, and was clearly influenced by the work of the Ferrarese artist Scarsellino.

However, as Guercino was several times reported to have himself acknowledged, he also owed a debt to an important altar-piece, the *Madonna and Child with Sts Francis and Joseph with a donor*, painted in 1591 by Ludovico Carracci (1555-1619) for the Capuchin church in Cento and now in the Pinacoteca at Cento. The affinity between much of Guercino's early work and this painting make it clear that Ludovico Carracci's work influenced Guercino deeply. The admiration became mutual, as is made clear in a letter written by the aged Ludovico in 1617 in which he warmly praises Guercino's work.[2] Ludovico's letter also makes clear that Guercino had never formally been his pupil. Works of the kind that Ludovico could have admired are nos.1 and 2 in the present catalogue, which date from around 1615-17.

Apart from Bologna, Guercino also visited Venice (1618), Ferrara (1619 and 1620) and Mantua (1620), and it is possible that he went also to other nearby towns such as Modena and Parma, where he could have seen the work of Correggio. It was during these last years of the decade that he was introduced to some of his most important early patrons. Cardinal Serra, Papal Legate (that is to say Governor) of Ferrara, much admired Guercino's paintings and commissioned a group of large canvases that are among his finest works (see nos.8 and 9 in this catalogue). The Cardinal Archbishop of Bologna, Alessandro Ludovisi, as well as other members of that prominent Bolognese family were commissioning work from Guercino by 1617 (see under cat.no.17). And in 1620 Guercino painted a work for the Duke of Mantua (cat.no.6). In spite of this success he continued to work in Cento until, in 1621, he went to Rome.

Alessandro Ludovisi had been elected Pope on 9th February 1621, taking the name Gregory XV (see cat.no.17). He quickly appointed his art-loving nephew, Ludovico, to be a Cardinal, and brought to Rome as his secretary the scholar

Fig. 1. *Self-portrait*. Oil on canvas, 65 by 70.5 cm. (Richard L. Feigen, London).

Monsignor Giovanni Battista Agucchi. Agucchi was keenly interested in the arts, having been a close friend of Annibale Carracci and the champion of another Bolognese painter, Domenichino (whose portrait of Agucchi is in York City Art Gallery). Domenichino was himself patronised by the Ludovisi family and was soon summoned to Rome. Guercino was also asked to go there, and left Cento on 12th May 1621. The portrait he painted of Pope Gregory while there is in the J. Paul Getty Museum, Malibu, California. He stayed in Rome for just over two years, leaving shortly after the death of Pope Gregory, which occurred on 8th July 1623.

The two years Guercino spent in Rome were busy ones. While it is unclear exactly how many small commissions he undertook, the major ones are all well documented. The most important to be completed was the vast altar-piece of the *Burial and Reception into Heaven of St Petronilla* which he painted for the basilica of St Peter's and signed in 1623 (it is now in the Capitoline Museum, Rome). He also carried out several ceiling decorations, of which the most notable is the justly famous *Aurora* in Casino Ludovisi, a villa acquired in 1621 by the newly appointed Cardinal Ludovisi; others were at Palazzo Patrizi (now Palazzo Costaguti) and Palazzo

Lancellotti. These commissions indicate the importance of Guercino's patrons in Rome. Apart from the St Petronilla altar-piece, the most important religious commission Guercino received was from Cardinal Scipione Borghese for the ceiling on canvas for the church of San Crisogono (see cat.no.13).

Guercino must also have seen a great deal of stimulating painting in Rome, much of it contemporary. Indeed these two years should be regarded as crucial in his artistic development. Yet, though a fundamental reorientation did occur, the consequences of this in his own art seem to have been gradual. The striking use of light in Guercino's early work has often given rise to comparisons with the paintings of Caravaggio. But it should be remembered that Guercino is most unlikely to have seen any of Caravaggio's works before he went to Rome; and that the paintings of Caravaggio, who died in 1610 but who had left Rome as early as 1606, were becoming less influential when Guercino was there.

In any case there is a fundamental difference between the art of Caravaggio and that of Guercino. Whereas the former used highly dramatic effects to clarify the subject matter of his naturalistic works (and they were often criticised for being so), Guercino used light in a very different way; in many of his early paintings the subjects can sometimes be almost obscured by the subtle pictorial effects he achieved. Rather than being specifically influenced by a single painter during his Roman sojourn, Guercino seems to have absorbed various aspects of Roman art, both classical and contemporary; although these began to surface in his work immediately, their full effect became apparent only much later. It seems that with the prospects of the patronage of the Papal family (which were, however, dashed by the Pope's early death) and with the encouragement of Monsignor Agucchi, Guercino had begun to consider the possibilities of changing certain aspects of his style.

While it is simple to perceive the difference between early and late works (compare, say, cat.nos.9 and 27), in the paintings of the period immediately after Guercino's return from Rome such differences are rather more difficult to discern. However, in passages such as the upper part of the *St Chrysogonus* (cat.no.13), where the musical angels are illuminated in a much more even manner than the figures in the lower part of the painting, a certain change is already becoming apparent. Another painting where the transition from his earlier style is noticeable is the *Presentation of Jesus in the Temple* of 1623 (cat.no.14) where the figures are ranged across the composition in an almost frieze-like manner, giving a greater clarity to the narrative.

By the time he returned from Rome to Cento, at the age of thirty-two, his reputation was very high indeed, and not solely in Italy. In 1626 King Charles I of England, after attempting in vain to secure the services of Guido Reni, then the most renowned Italian painter, tried to persuade Guercino to visit London (see p.4 below). Similar attempts were made by Louis XIII of France, again without success. In 1629 Guercino was visited at Cento by the great Spanish painter, Velázquez. One of the reasons for the latter's Italian journey was to try to secure the services of important Italian painters to work at the court of Philip IV in Madrid. It is possible, although there is no evidence, that Velázquez may have considered attempting to lure Guercino to Madrid. However that may be, it is clear that Guercino had no wish to travel. Indeed he had no need for extra or more prestigious work, for commissions continued to arrive.

Guercino worked prolifically for the rest of his career. While he personally was responsible for all the works in this exhibition, his workshop did include a number of artists, notably belonging to the Gennari family (related to him by the marriage of his sister), who often made copies before his originals were despatched to clients (see under cat.no.22) and may occasionally have been allowed to help him marginally on works for the less prominent or wealthy of his patrons. But his life seems to have been comparatively quiet. He was visited by princes, cardinals, dukes and many nobles (even by Queen Christina of Sweden in 1655), and it is significant that they went to him and not he to them. The most important event in the later part of Guercino's life took place in 1642 when, after the death of Guido Reni in Bologna in that year, and with the advent of threatening military activity close to Cento, he moved permanently to Bologna, buying a house there in 1644. He remained in that city as its leading painter until his death in 1666, and was buried in the Bolognese church of S. Salvatore, the church to which his champion in his early days and lifelong friend, Padre Mirandola, had been attached.

[1]Malvasia, a Bolognese aristocrat, cleric and lawyer, was a great connoisseur, and a champion of the Bolognese school of painting. His biography of Guercino – the most important early source for the artist's life and works – is in his two-volume book, *Felsina Pittrice* published in 1678, which also contains biographies of most of the principal seventeenth-century Bolognese painters, many of whom he knew personally. Guercino's *Libro dei Conti* was published in 1808 in Jacopo Alessandro Calvi's *Notizie della vita e delle opere del Cavalier Giovan Francesco Barbieri detto il Guercino da Cento*, and Calvi's redaction of it was incorporated into the second edition of Malvasia's *Felsina Pittrice* which appeared in 1841. For details of all these see under CALVI and MALVASIA in the Bibliographical Abbreviations on p.68 below.

Modern scholarship on Guercino and his works depends on the pioneering work of Sir Denis Mahon, whose *Studies in Seicento Art and Theory* of 1947 and detailed catalogue of the Guercino exhibition held in Bologna in 1968 remain seminal works, and who assisted Luigi Salerno in compiling what is now the standard catalogue raisonné of the artist's works, published in Italian in 1988 (see MAHON 1947, MAHON 1968 and SALERNO in the Select Bibliography). Other recent publications include Denis Mahon's and Nicholas Turner's catalogue of the drawings at Windsor Castle the catalogue by Stéphane Loire of the exhibition *Le Guerchin en France* held at the Louvre, Paris, in 1900, and the catalogue by Nicholas Turner and Carol Plazzotta of the exhibition *Drawings by Guercino from British Collections* being held at the British Museum from 17th May to 18th August 1991. Denis Mahon is also preparing the catalogue of the major exhibition of Guercino's work scheduled to take place later in 1991 (at Bologna and Cento, Frankfurt-am-Main, and in 1992 at Washington) which will update much of his own work of 1968.

[2]See MAHON 1968, p.45.

FRANCIS RUSSELL

Guercino and England

No painter of the Seicento has come to be more closely associated with English collections and English scholarship than Giovanni Francesco Barbieri, il Guercino. Yet England had no appeal for the man. His reputation led, in 1625-26, to an invitation to work for King Charles I on generous terms. As we hear from his biographer, Carlo Cesare Malvasia, Guercino's reaction was uncompromising:

> He did not wish to accept the opportunity, not desiring to converse with heretics, so as not to contaminate the goodness of his angelic habits, and also to avoid exposing himself to such a disastrous voyage, in a climate so remote from his own people.[1]

Guercino's religious scruples and his suspicions about travelling and the English weather were compounded by a strong sense of commitment to his own family and his native town of Cento, a commitment from which the British Royal collection was nevertheless indirectly to benefit in a spectacular fashion during the next century.

Despite his invitation, Charles I's admiration for Guercino's work cannot have been intense. In 1626, an agent secured two pictures for him in Rome, a landscape and a *Prophet Elias*. Neither inspired the King to buy any other works by the artist, and in the inventories of 1649-51 the two were valued at no more than five and two pounds respectively. Guercino's suspicions of England were not so set as to exclude his taking as pupil a youth of English extraction, Matteo Loves, who settled at Cento. His own nephew, pupil and co-heir, Benedetto Gennari, was to work for King Charles II for some years, arriving in England in 1674. The restored King had received an early masterpiece by Guercino, the *Semiramis* of 1624 (Fig.2) with the Dutch gift of 1660: this he presumably gave to his mistress, Barbara Villiers, Duchess of Cleveland, and it remained in the possession of her descendants, the Dukes of Grafton, until 1948.[2] Subsequently Gennari also worked for King James II, whom he followed into exile in France. Among his other patrons was the 4th Earl, subsequently 1st Duke, of Devonshire, one of the architects of James II's downfall: as Sir Denis Mahon has suggested, the presence at Chatsworth of an outstanding series of landscape drawings by Guercino may be owing to this association. Guercino's drawings were indeed highly prized in England from the seventeenth century, and found an inescapable place in the cabinets of almost every great collector from Peter Lely onwards.

Interest in Guercino's drawings may well have been encouraged by Roger de Piles, whose *Cours de Peinture* was widely read in Britain, and translated into English as *The Principles of Painting* in 1743. By de Piles's system of grading the masters, Guercino shared with Rubens alone the honour of receiving the maximum possible score, 18, for 'Composition'. Along with Holbein, Veronese and Dürer he received 10 for 'Design', and 10 for 'Colouring' – again the same as Dürer – though a mere 4 for 'Expression' in the company of such artists as Giorgione, Tintoretto and Leonardo. For Jonathan Richardson, Guercino ranked with Rubens, Spagnoletto (i.e. Ribera), Poussin, Cortona and Claude, 'great men in their several ways',[3] who yet marked a visible decline in the arts from the age of the Carracci. A later eighteenth-century critic, Matthew Pilkington, who drew extensively on de Piles, but had a clearer sense of the influences that had formed the artist and of his preoccupations with the fall of light and colour, concluded by observing that in all Guercino's works 'there is a powerful and expressive imitation of life, which will for ever render them estimable'.[4]

Despite interest in his drawings, Guercino's pictures were not well represented in Britain in the early eighteenth century. Attributions in any case were often unreliable, although not often so wide of the mark as Fougeroux's ascription to Guercino in 1728 of the Wilton *Shepherd and Shepherdess*, which has more recently been given to Bloemaert.[5] Lord Burlington, as Fougeroux records, owned the *Agony in the Garden* (cat.no.23), later at Chatsworth and now at Cardiff; the popularity of the composition is also attested by a copy which Horace Walpole saw at Redlynch. George Vertue noted paintings by Guercino at Cassiobury and in the Halifax collection; others were at Foots Cray, at Devonshire House and in the collections of Sir Paul Methuen and Dr Mead. But, significantly, Guercino was an absentee from the great picture collections assembled by Sir Robert Walpole and the 1st Earl of Leicester, although the latter owned a fine group of his drawings.

The first major altar-piece by Guercino to reach England was the *St Luke painting the Virgin* now at Kansas City (Fig.4), which is recorded in the Spencer collection in 1750. A year later, an archetypal Whig magnate, the 2nd Marquess

Fig.2. *Semiramis*. 1624. Oil on canvas, 112 by 155 cm. (Museum of Fine Arts, Boston).

of Rockingham, acquired the *Hagar and Ishmael* now in the Mahon Collection (cat.no.32). It is not difficult to see why such masterpieces of Guercino's later years appealed to a generation that venerated Guido Reni. In the early 1760s King George III bought the exquisite *Libyan Sibyl* (cat.no.31) of the same period, to complement the extraordinary series of drawings secured for him by Richard Dalton from Casa Gennari.[6] Zoffany no doubt recalled the picture when including the workshop replica of the pendant, the *Samian Sibyl*, acquired by the Grand Duke of Tuscany in 1777, in his picture of the *Tribuna of the Uffizi* (Royal Collections), painted for Queen Charlotte.

Bartolozzi's prints after drawings from Casa Gennari were executed to publicise their acquisition by George III, and were prompt to evoke a response in England. Between 1762 and 1764 William Wynne Rylands engraved copies of Guercino drawings owned by the sculptor Rysbrack, by the painters Hudson and Reynolds, and by Lord Cholmondeley and the connoisseur Charles Rogers, whose *A Collection of Prints in Imitation of Drawings*, published in 1778 contained nine after the master out of a total of 98. That Guercino was so well represented among the collections of artists was not accidental. In his youth Reynolds made copies of drawings by Guercino owned by his master Hudson and of others in the collection acquired by John Bouverie from Casa Gennari.[7] Later Reynolds would himself own both drawings and pictures by the artist. An early copy of the *Madonna and Child with the Infant St John* now at Edinburgh (cat.no.2), was engraved as in his collection in 1766 and was apparently retouched by him; he subsequently sold it to his patron Lord Boringdon for Saltram where it remains. Sir Joshua was, of course, well known for his dependence on earlier prototypes. In 1768 the young Lord Carlisle thought he had identified such a borrowing in the portrait of *Lady Sarah Bunbury sacrificing to the Graces*, now in the Art Institute in Chicago:

> I saw, in a cupola at Piacenza, an angel very like ———; I am sure Reynolds must have taken the idea of his picture from it. You may easily fancy that such a resemblance would not escape me.[8]

However Reynolds may have responded to the Piacenza frescoes, there can be no doubt that he was closely familiar with Guercino's stylistic evolution. In his fourteenth Discourse, writing of the advantages of painting by candlelight, he observed:

> . . . I am more assured, that whoever attentively studies the first and best manner of Guercino, will be convinced that he either painted by this light, or formed his manner on this conception.[9]

Sir Joshua clearly had studied works by Guercino when in Italy. In the years of his own ascendancy as a portrait painter the holdings of pictures by the Italian master in British collections were transformed: Lord Tavistock bought the Barberini *Samson taking the Honey to his Father* now in the Chrysler Museum (Fig.3) in 1764; while Gavin Hamilton

Fig.3. *Samson taking the Honey to his Father*. c.1625. Oil on canvas, 101 by 150 cm. (Chrysler Museum, Norfolk, Virginia, gift of Walter P. Chrysler, Jr., in honour of the Boards of Trustees, 1977-85).

acquired two late masterpieces, the *Samian Sibyl* and *King David* (cat.nos.28 and 29) for the 1st Earl Spencer in 1768; happily these are still at Althorp.[10] The Dunham Massey *Venus, Mars, Cupid and Time* (cat.no.16), is known to have been in the Stamford collection in 1769, and the second major altar-piece to reach Britain, the *Assumption of the Virgin*, now in Detroit (Fig.7) was acquired by the 3rd Earl of Bute, probably in the late 1760s and certainly before 1776. In 1772 the 5th Earl of Carlisle spent the then substantial sum of 500 guineas at Christie's on the *Erminia finding the Wounded Tancred* (cat.no.30), and the 3rd Earl Cowper, an equally demanding connoisseur, bought his *St Jerome* (S.251; Harris Collection, New York) in 1778;[11] the extraordinary Aldrovandi *Portrait of a Dog* (Norton Simon Museum, Pasadena; S.104) was probably also acquired by John Smith Barry of Marbury in the 1770s

Fig.4. *St Luke painting the Virgin*. 1653. Oil on canvas, 221 by 181 cm. (Nelson Atkins Museum of Art, Kansas City).

A decade later the outbreak of the French Revolution heralded changes in the world of collecting that few can have foreseen. Within a few years the fate of the greatest private collection in France after that of the King himself, that of the Duke of Orléans, was at stake; in the 1790s the purchase of this by the Duke of Bridgewater and his associates would bring both the large *David and Abigail* (S.161), destroyed at Bridgewater House during the last war, and the flawless *Presentation* (cat.no.14), which was to fetch 520 guineas in the saleroom in 1802.

Splendid as such pictures were, they would be outshone by those that came to Britain as a result of the French invasion of Italy. French officials appropriated altar-pieces by Guercino with characteristic fervour and with results that enrich the Louvre and many a provincial museum in France today.[12] Patrician collections were affected by different pressures and of these Britain was for half a century the main beneficiary. Pictures from the great Roman collections, Borghese and Colonna, Aldobrandini and Lancellotti, from the Balbi and Mari of Genoa and many others would come to England.

Such agents and dealers as Tresham and Fagan, Irvine and Wilson, scoured Italy, for the most part on profitable terms. In England a leading rôle was taken by the dealer William Buchanan, whose correspondence with Irvine is an illuminating commentary on their activities. Irvine offered a series of major pictures but Buchanan sought to restrain him with sage advice: 'The pictures of Guercino do not appear to sell well here, he is thought too brickey in his shadows'.[13] Moreover, despite the brief reprieve from war afforded by the Peace of Amiens, there was a shortage of buyers for expensive works. Thus in 1803 Buchanan could congratulate Irvine on resisting as a 'very bad speculation'[14] the *Entombment* now at Chicago (Fig.5), for which £1,000 had previously been asked and which would fetch no more than 430 guineas in 1812. That Buchanan's taste lay elsewhere – in 1805 he admitted that the ex-Orléans *Presentation* (cat.no.14) and the *Holy Family* now at Cleveland (Fig.6) were the only Guercinos he 'ever thought much of'[15] – did not restrain his sense of salesmanship. As late as 1840 he thought unsuccessfully to impose the *Assumption of the Virgin* now in the Hermitage, Leningrad (S.99), on George Lucy for the hall at Charlecote, on the premise that it could 'be seen in all its parts at a mile's distance'.[16]

The cumulative results of the hard-headed activities of Buchanan and his contemporaries were impressive. Masterpieces from every phase of Guercino's development came to Britain, but his earlier work was particularly well represented; the two early landscapes from the Aldobrandini collection, one of which is now at Stockholm (S.19 and 20); the exquisite Borghese *Lamentation* (cat.no.4); the *Madonna of the Sparrow* from the same source (cat.no.1); and, above all, the *Glory of St Chrysogonus* (cat.no.13), which Day acquired from its original setting at Rome by 1808. After being bought in at Christie's for 745 guineas in 1833, this was sold to the 2nd Duke of

Sutherland who installed it as a ceiling at Stafford House, now Lancaster House, where it remains. The Duke's appreciation of the artist led to his purchase of another masterpiece, the *St Gregory* altar-piece (cat.no.17), now in the Mahon collection, which had left Spain as a result of the French invasion. Another major altar-piece reached England in rather different circumstances. The *Vision of S. Luigi Gonzaga*, now in the Metropolitan Museum (Fig.9), had been appropriated by Marshal Junot, who himself sent it to sale at Christie's in 1817. It failed to sell at 350 guineas but went to Woodburn for 190 a year later. Woodburn sold it to John Grant, elder brother of Francis Grant who was to be so successful a portrait painter, but, as John was a minor, his father could repudiate the purchase; in 1821 Grant, now of age, traced the picture in Milan and finally secured it. If the S. Luigi Gonzaga altar-piece had disappointed Junot in 1817, he must have been equally dismayed by the lack of interest in his other 'Guercino', the *Miracle of St Francis Xavier*, now in that saint's church in Paris, which failed at a mere 36 guineas: even if had it not suffered from the disadvantage of being by Benedetto Gennari, the subject – a crustacean retrieving a crucifix which the saint had dropped overboard – would have seemed too silly to be taken seriously by an English audience.

Guercino was represented in exhibitions at the British Institution, and in 1830 its sister body, the Royal Institution of Edinburgh, authorised the purchase of two characteristic Guercinos, the *Madonna and Child with the Infant St John* (cat.no.2) and the *Penitent St Peter* (cat.no.22), in Genoa and Florence respectively. Perhaps because of the Rev. W. Holwell Carr's bequest in 1831 of the Borghese *Lamentation* (cat.no.4), no such step was considered necessary by the National Gallery.

The publication of Dr Waagen's *Works of Art and Artists in England* in 1838 allowed for the first time a comprehensive view of collections in this country. Waagen's opinions, which would be restated in 1854, were to have a subtle influence on the changing pattern of taste. Guercino remained a great master, but not a flawless one. The Borghese *Lamentation* was 'equally commendable for the lively feeling which is not common in this master, the beauty of the composition, the clearness and depth of the powerful colouring, and the finished execution'.[17] The Althorp *St Luke* was 'very modern in conception'.[18] But the Sutherland *St Chrysogonus*, incorrectly identified as St Paul, although of 'powerful effect' and 'executed in a masterly manner' was 'rather coarse in the character of the heads and wanting expression'.[19] The heads of the Bridgewater House *David and Abigail* were 'uniform and unmeaning' and the 'effect' had become 'specky and inharmonious in consequence of the darkening of the shadows'.[20] Worse still, the Castle Howard *Tancred and Erminia* (cat.no.30) was 'without style in the composition, and destitute of spirit' although 'carefully painted in a glowing rather reddish tone'.[21] Late works by the artist, in particular, suffered as layers of dirt and discoloured varnish masked their chromatic subtlety.

One of the last of the long series of imports from Italy, the *Esther and Ahasuerus*, now at Ann Arbor (Fig.8), arrived in 1856 with the collection of Pietro Camuccini which was purchased *en bloc* by the 4th Duke of Northumberland for Alnwick. A year later Guercino would be represented by fourteen pictures in the great *Art Treasures Exhibition* at Manchester. These included the Borghese *Madonna* (cat.no.1), lent by Miss Burdett Coutts, the philanthropist. The fact that a 'repetition' of the National Gallery *Lamentation*, almost certainly a copy, was considered the finest Guercino in the exhibition by George Scharf suggests how little the master's true qualities were now understood.[22]

When visiting Milan in 1816, Byron had expressed his admiration for Guercino's *Hagar and Ishmael* in the Brera (Fig.10): 'Of painting I know nothing', he wrote to his publisher Murray, 'but I like the Guercino – a painting of Abraham putting away Hagar – & Ishmael – which seems to me natural and goodly.'[23] But Byron was one of the last nineteenth-century Englishmen to take this view of Guercino. The re-evaluation of early Italian art brought with it a

Fig.5. *Entombment*. 1656. Oil on canvas, 146.7 by 221.2 cm. (Art Institute, Chicago, Wilson L. Mead Fund, 1956. 128).

Fig.6. *Holy Family*. 1624. Oil on canvas, 68.5 cm. diameter. (Museum of Art, Cleveland, Mr and Mrs William H. Marlatt Fund, 67. 123).

Fig.7. *Assumption of the Virgin*. 1650. Oil on canvas, 301.5 by 221 cm. (Institute of Arts, Detroit Purchase: Founders Society, Robert H. Tannahill Foundation and Josephine & Ernest Kanzler Founders Fund).

revulsion against the entire Bolognese school. The very same picture which appeared natural to Byron seemed revoltingly unspiritual to John Ruskin forty years later: 'The grief of Guercino's Hagar, in the Brera Gallery at Milan', he wrote in *Modern Painters*, 'is partly despicable, partly disgusting, partly ridiculous; it is not the grief of the injured Egyptian, driven forth into the desert with the destiny of a nation in her heart; but of a servant of all work turned away for stealing tea and sugar.'[24] In his *Academy notes* of 1858 Ruskin compared 'the vile Guercino of Milan' unfavourably with a painting of the same subject by the now forgotten W.C.T. Dobson.[25]

Writing a generation later, John Addington Symonds, while he deplored the 'clangour of exaggeration' of Ruskin's denunciations of Italian painting of this period, and found the vicissitudes of taste that had dethroned the Bolognese perplexing, nonetheless concluded that the modern view represented 'a wholesome reaction . . . to academical dogmatism'. But Symonds's account of Guercino is not wholly unsympathetic. Though his comparison of the artist's 'buttery impasto' to Bolognese sausage is a cheap jibe, and his assessment of the 'frigid inhumanity' of the *Hagar* a received Ruskinian view, nonetheless he was alive to Guercino's qualities as a colourist, even if he denied him Michelangelo's *terribilità*. 'The terrible takes in Guercino's work far lower flights than in the Sistine Chapel. With Michelangelo it soared like an eagle; with Guercino it flitted like a bat. His brawny saints are ponderous, not awe-inspiring.'[25]

Given this reversal of Guercino's critical fortunes, it is uncertain what construction should be placed on the acquisition for Dublin of the *St Joseph* (S.171) in 1882. At 23½ guineas it cannot have been considered expensive, although even in 1815, when Henry Tresham had tried to dispose of it, the picture had languished without a buyer at 85 guineas. An equally exceptional phenomenon was the purchase for the

Fig.8. *Esther and Ahasuerus*. 1639. Oil on canvas, 159.6 by 217 cm. (University of Michigan Museum of Art, Ann Arbor).

National Gallery of the superlative *Incredulity of St Thomas* (cat.no.10) for fifty guineas at the Hope sale in 1917. No Seicento picture had been bought for the gallery since 1864 and, with the exception of an insignificant copy, none would follow until 1941. Roger Fry might pronounce that Guercino 'must be accounted a scientific, if not an inspired master' although admitting 'a virility and force' in the *Vision of St Bruno* (S.241) at Bologna.[27] But Captain Langton Douglas, who was the intermediary by which so many more fashionable masterpieces crossed the Atlantic, had the perception to buy the *Taking of Christ* (cat.no.11), which he gave to the Fitzwilliam in 1924. The *Taking* had cost thirteen guineas at the Hope sale, and prices of this order would remain the norm for many years.

Change nonetheless was on the way. In 1933, Denis Mahon, who had just come down from Oxford, attended lectures at the newly-founded Courtauld Institute by among others Nikolaus Pevsner, who gave a series about Italian Baroque Painting. He arranged to have private tutorials with Pevsner, and finally asked which painter he should study: 'Why not Guercino?' was the response. No reader of this catalogue will need to be told about Sir Denis's subsequent contribution to the study of the Seicento or of his rôle in a now legendary sequence of exhibitions in Bologna that has left so deep an influence on the perceptions of other scholars. But no survey of Guercino and Britain would be complete without reference to the Mahon collection. Sir Denis's first picture by Guercino was the outstanding *Jacob blessing the Sons of Joseph* (cat.no.8), which he purchased in 1934 when it resurfaced in Paris. This was followed in 1936 by the *Elijah fed by Ravens* (cat.no.9), which had been sold by the Barberini. By then Mahon was an honorary attaché at the National Gallery, and with characteristic punctilio he offered to surrender the picture at cost price: Sir Kenneth Clark, who himself admired it, pronounced that the trustees would

Fig.9. *Vision of S. Luigi Gonzaga*. 1650-51. Oil on canvas, 356 by 269 cm. (Metropolitan Museum of Art, New York, gift of Mr and Mrs Charles Wrightsman, 1973; 1973. 311. 3).

Fig.10. *Hagar and Ishmael*. 1657-58. Oil on canvas, 115 by 154 cm. (Pinacoteca di Brera, Milan).

Fig.11. *Joseph and Potiphar's wife*. 1649-50. Oil on canvas, 124.3 by 157.7 cm. (National Gallery of Art, Washington D.C.).

Fig.12. *Amnon and Tamar*. 1649-50. Oil on canvas, 123.5 by 158.7 cm. (National Gallery of Art, Washington D.C.).

never agree to such a purchase, although the sum in question was very modest. A series of masterpieces followed: the *St Gregory* altar-piece (cat.no.17) in 1941; the *Madonna of the sparrow* in 1946 (cat.no.1); the *Hagar* from Wentworth Woodhouse in 1948 (cat.no.32); the *Presentation* from Ashburnham in 1953 (cat.no.14); the Sempill *Cumaean Sibyl* in 1954 (cat.no.27); and, last, the *St John the Baptist in Prison visited by Salome* from Bowood in 1964 (cat.no.15).

Much of the Mahon collection was shown in 1960 at the memorable *Italian Art and Britain* exhibition at the Royal Academy, which in effect re-introduced Guercino to an English audience. It is reasonable to see Birmingham's inspired acquisition of *Erminia and the Shepherd* (cat.no.6) in 1962 as a response. But, alas, it must be admitted that Sir Denis's lead was not followed by other institutions in this country. By contrast since 1948, when the Grafton *Semiramis* was bought for Boston, North American museums have bought some two dozen pictures by Guercino from British collections: Chicago in 1956; Mr and Mrs Wrightsman, with the Metropolitan Museum in mind, and Greenville in 1957; Ann Arbor, Phoenix, Ottawa, San Francisco, Cleveland and Kansas City in the 1960s; Detroit, Pasadena (twice), Houston and Austin in the 1970s; and more recently San Diego, Kansas City again and Washington. Many of the pictures in question represent facets of Guercino's personality that cannot be experienced in this exhibition, not least the haunting *Jacob and Potiphar's Wife* and its charged pendant *Amnon and Tamar* (Figs.11 and 12) from Wynyard that passed to Washington in 1986.

It is sobering to realise that if Sir Denis Mahon's scholarship had not been matched by a taste for collecting as determined as that of any connoisseur of the eighteenth or nineteenth centuries, it would now be too late to hold a serious exhibition of pictures in this country by Guercino.[28]

[1]'. . . *non volle accettar l'occasione, non volendo conversar con eretici, per non contaminar la bontà de'suoi angelici costumi, & anco per non esporsi a viaggio così disastroso, in clima così lontano da'suoi.*' (C.C. MALVASIA: *Felsina pittrice*, Bologna [1678], p.366; [1841], p.261.)

[2]See D. MAHON: 'Guercino's Paintings of Semiramis', *Art Bulletin*, [1949], p.221.

[3]*The Works of Mr Jonathan Richardson*, London [1773], p.289.

[4]M. PILKINGTON: *A General Dictionary of Painters*, London [1770], p.38.

[5]P.J. FOUGEROUX: *Voyage d'Angleterre d'Hollande et de Flandre*, 1728, MS, Victoria and Albert Museum, London, *sub* Wilton.

[6]Jane Roberts has drawn my attention to a note from George III to the 3rd Earl of Bute, which supplements the comprehensive account of the acquisition of the Guercino drawings at Windsor given in D. MAHON and N. TURNER: *The Drawings of Guercino in the Collection of Her Majesty the Queen at Windsor Castle*, Cambridge [1989], pp.xxii-xxxiv. The letter reads: 'My D. Friend: I have this instant receiv'd from Dalton the collection of Guercinos you gave him for me. They were very beautiful, but their value is much encreased from the pleasure of whenever I examine them that must occur, of knowing from whom I have got them. Wednesday.' (Mount Stuart MSS, King George III to the 3rd Earl of Bute, no.401.)

[7]See N. TURNER and C. PLAZZOTTA: *Drawings by Guercino from British Collections*, exh.cat., British Museum, London [1991], pp.21-26.

[8]J.H. JESSE: *George Selwyn and His Contemporaries; with Memoirs and Notes*, London [1843-44], II, p.292.

[9]R.R. WARK, ed.: *Sir Joshua Reynolds. Discourses on Art*, New Haven and London [1975], Discourse XIV, p.251.

[10]An earlier dealing activity of Hamilton deserves investigation. In 1764 James Martin reported that Hamilton had bought a group of Guercino drawings (information from Sir Brinsley Ford's Archive of British visitors to Italy, Paul Mellon Centre for British Art, London).

[11]Numerical references in the text prefaced by 'S.' refer to L. SALERNO: *I Dipinti del Guercino*, Rome [1988].

[12]See most recently S. LOIRE: *Le Guerchin en France*, exh.cat., Musée du Louvre, Paris [1990].

[13]H. BRIGSTOCKE: *William Buchanan and the 19th Century Art Trade: 100 Letters to his Agents in London and Italy*, London [1982], p.73.

[14]*Ibid.*, p.91.

[15]*Ibid.*, p.403.

[16]*Ibid.*, p.32.

[17]G.A. WAAGEN: *Works of Art and Artists in England*, London [1838], Vol.I, p.211.

[18]*Ibid.*, Vol.III, p.332.

[19]*Ibid.*, Vol.II, p.248.

[20]*Ibid.*, Vol.II, p.56.

[21]*Ibid.*, Vol.III, p.208.

[22] [G. SCHARF]: *A Handbook to the Paintings by Ancient Masters in the Art Treasures Exhibition*, London [1857], p.44.

[23]Letter to John Murray, 15th October 1816; see L.A. MARCHAND, ed.: *Byron's Letters and Journals*, Vol.V, London [1976], p.116.

[24]J. RUSKIN: *Modern Painters*, Vol.II, Part III, Section I, Chapter XIV [1846]; in *Collected Works*, ed. E.T. COOK and A. WEDDERBURN, London [1903-12], Vol.IV, p.157.

[25]*Idem*: 'Academy Notes No.IV. 1858', in *Collected Works*, cited above, Vol.XIV, p.157.

[26]J.A. SYMONDS: *The Renaissance in Italy*, Vol.VII, *The Catholic Reaction*, Part II, London [1898], pp.218-27; first published [1886].

[27]See *Discourses by Sir Joshua Reynolds, Kt. with introductions and notes by Roger Fry*, London [1905], opposite plate xiv.

[28]I am greatly indebted to Sir Denis Mahon for offering information and advice with characteristic generosity.

Catalogue

Cat.no.1

1. *Madonna of the Sparrow*

c.1615-16

Lent by Sir Denis Mahon CBE FBA.

Canvas. 78.5 by 58 cm. Inscribed at bottom on the left are the traces of the number 105.

Prov.: In the Borghese collection, Rome, before 1693; inventoried, as bearing the number '105', in the collection of Giovanni Battista Borghese, Principe di Rossano, on 7th April 1693 (from which it is clear that the number 105 relates to an earlier, but untraced, Borghese inventory); recorded as still in the Palazzo Borghese in 1798; from where acquired in 1799-1800 by William Young Ottley who offered the picture for sale in London in 1801; sold from the Morland collection, 1820, when purchased by Samuel Rogers; purchased at the Rogers sale in 1856 by Miss Burdett-Coutts, whose name is inscribed on the stretcher; acquired by Denis Mahon in 1946.

Lit.: MAHON 1968, pp.35-36, no.13; *England and the Seicento*, exh.cat., Agnews, London [1973], no.30; *Nell' Età di Correggio e dei Carracci*, exh.cat., Bologna [1986], p.461, no.159; SALERNO, p.97, no.18; MAHON 1991.

In representations of the Madonna and Child, a bird can constitute a symbolic reference to the Passion. Its presence here, in Guercino's *Holy Family* at Florence (MAHON 1968, pp.34-35, no.12), and those drawings of the period, such as that in the Cini Foundation, Venice (MAHON 1969, p.48, no.15) in all of which the motif of a bird attached to a string reappears, may be related to this tradition.

The intimate, every-day, realism of the well-observed rendering of the subject, and the solidity of the forms are characteristic of the strong emerging personality of the young Guercino – always sensitive to the mother and child relationship implicit in pictures of the Madonna and Child. Simplicity of this kind cannot easily be found later in Guercino's early period, and the picture is likely to date from 1615-16 when the artist was in his mid-twenties. The Madonna is still reminiscent of the figure in Ludovico Carracci's 1591 altar-piece, which Guercino is known to have admired in the Capuchin church at Cento (it is now in the Pinacoteca Civica there), but the lighting is more controlled than in other very early works, and the general effect may owe something to treatments of the Madonna subject by Bartolommeo Schedoni (1578-1615).

2. *Virgin and Sleeping Child with the Infant St John*

c.1616-17

National Galleries of Scotland, Edinburgh (no.40).

Canvas. 86 by 110.5 cm.

Prov.: Acquired from the De Franchi family, Genoa, by the Royal Institution, Edinburgh in 1830. Transferred to the National Gallery of Scotland, 1858. There is a copy at Saltram House (probably that engraved in reverse by John Hamilton Mortimer in 1766 as in the collection of Sir Joshua Reynolds).

Lit.: MAHON 1968, pp.36-37, no.14; H. BRIGSTOCKE: *Italian and Spanish Paintings in the National Gallery of Scotland*, Edinburgh [1978], p.62, no.40; SALERNO, p.100, no.22; MAHON 1991.

The Virgin Mary and the Child Jesus with the young St John the Baptist is a traditional subject in Italian painting, having originated in the fifteenth century. Guercino, who was ever alive to the human element in his subject matter and was a particularly keen observer of mother and child relationships, has chosen to depict the Virgin helping (or perhaps teaching) St John to read the words 'EC[CE]AGNU[S DEI]' (Behold the Lamb of God) with which he later identified Jesus (see John, 1:29-36). The identification of Jesus as the Lamb of God alludes to His sacrifice for mankind on the cross, and the analogy with Jesus Christ was adopted by the Early Christian church. In Christian tradition the sleep of Christ also foreshadows His death and the way Jesus lies across His mother's lap here draws upon the imagery of the Lamentation or *Pietà*.

Although Mahon (1968) and Salerno dated this picture to c.1615-16, then considering it earlier than the altar-piece of the *Madonna and Child with Sts Joseph, Augustine, Louis and Francis* (Musées Royaux des Beaux-Arts, Brussels, SALERNO, p.110, no.27) of 1616, Mahon (following an oral suggestion of David Stone) now believes it to postdate that picture, particularly in view of its stylistic links with the *Madonna del Carmine with St Albert* in the Pinacoteca Civica at Cento (SALERNO, p.119, no.38) which is documented as having been completed in 1618 (see MAHON 1991).

3. *St Sebastian Succoured by Two Angels*

1617

Sudeley Castle, Gloucestershire.

Copper. 43 by 32.5 cm. Inscribed on verso: 'IO. FRANC. BARBERIVS A CENTO F/MDCXVII'.

Prov.: Probably sold from the collections of John Humble, 1812, and William Hastings, 1840; Morrison collection by 1857; and then by descent to the Basildon Pictures Settlement at Sudeley Castle.

Lit.: MAHON 1968, pp.44-45, note 3; *England and the Seicento*, exh.cat., Agnews, London [1973], no.31; BAGNI, *Incisori*, p.51; SALERNO, p.113, no.31; MAHON 1991.

Sebastian was one of the most venerated Christian martyrs. The traditional story of his martyrdom (as recounted by Jacopo da Voragine in his popular thirteenth-century compilation of lives of the Saints, the *Golden Legend*) was that, while serving as a soldier in Imperial Rome (c.300 AD), Sebastian was discovered to be a Christian and sentenced to death. The *Golden Legend* describes how Diocletian 'commanded him to be led to the field, and there to be bounden to a stake for to be shot at. And the archers shot at him till he was full of arrows as a sea-urchin is full of pricks, and thus left him there for dead'. He survived the arrows, and was eventually stoned to death.

St Sebastian succoured by angels is an unusual subject, and the episode does not appear in the *Golden Legend*. Throughout that text, as well as later Christian iconography, Sebastian's life (and death) was paralleled with that of Christ, and Guercino's development of the iconography of St Sebastian was perhaps prompted by his interest in the subject of Christ mourned. Guercino painted a *Dead Christ Mourned by Angels* (see cat.no.4 below) within a year or two of this *St Sebastian*. These two pictures are both on copper and are almost identical in size, and it might seem that Guercino thought of depicting *St Sebastian Succoured by Two Angels*, as a result of his contemporary consideration of the theme of the *Dead Christ Mourned by Angels*, and in the light of the traditional comparison of Sebastian with Christ. In 1619 Guercino painted the more conventional image of St Irene nursing St Sebastian, after his would-be executioners had left him for dead (see SALERNO, p.131, no.54 and also under cat.no.5 below).

Since Malvasia records no painting by Guercino of 1617, this exquisite small painting with its obviously authentic inscription and date provides a useful indication of how mature and sophisticated Guercino's methods of composition and lighting had become by that year. The existence of copies suggests that it enjoyed a certain celebrity, to which Pasqualini's engraving of 1623 must also have contributed.

4. *The Dead Christ Mourned by Two Angels*

c.1617-18

National Gallery, London (no.22).

Copper. 36.8 by 44.4 cm.

Prov.: In the Borghese collection before 1693; inventoried in the collection of Giovanni Battista Borghese, Principe di Rossano, 7th April 1693 (where it is recorded as being inscribed with the number 44, relating to an earlier and now untraced Borghese inventory). Sold by Prince Marcantonio IV Borghese shortly before his death in March 1800 to the dealer Durand, and so recorded in a list dated 9th April 1801. Next recorded in 1813 in the collection of Admiral Lord Radstock, from whom it was purchased by Holwell Carr. Bequeathed to the National Gallery by the Rev. W. Holwell Carr, 1831.

Lit.: MAHON 1968, pp.56-58, no.23; M. LEVEY: *The National Gallery Catalogues: The Seventeenth and Eighteenth Century Italian Schools*, London [1971], p.141; SALERNO, p.118, no.37; MAHON/TURNER, p.2, no.3; MAHON 1991.

This painting on copper is one of the finest and most successful of Guercino's small religious works. Its subject, Christ's body after His deposition from the Cross, is principally devotional, perhaps intended for private contemplation, and Guercino's fine touch and muted tones create a wonderful night scene. There is no New Testament source for an image of Christ being mourned by two angels, but two angels are described as emerging from his tomb on the morning after the Resurrection (John XX:11-17). Guercino may have chosen to imagine the preceding moment in the Passion when the angels mourned the dead Christ, but as the setting appears to be in the open air, the image may be related to the Lamentation of Christ's body at the foot of the Cross.

Guercino is remarkable for the strong, rich colour sense which he had already mastered early in his career. Light is used softly, but dramatically and even in this quiet picture it focuses attention upon Christ's body. The picture is intriguingly related to the *St Sebastian Succoured* (cat.no.3 above).

Three drawings have been related to this picture with considerable probability (see MAHON 1968, pp.56-58; LEVEY, p.142, and MAHON/TURNER no.3, p.2). Mahon and Turner observe that the doubts expressed over the relationship of the drawings to the finished picture can be allayed if one recognises that 'Guercino's preparatory studies for a projected painting frequently do not correspond, even in format, with the final solution, especially in the artist's early work'.

The composition's popularity is attested by the existence of many copies. Two other versions bore attributions to Guercino as early as the seventeenth century, but as neither can now be identified it is not known whether Guercino himself painted replicas of it.

5. *Study of a Woman, completed in the form of a Sibyl*

1619

Lent by Sir Denis Mahon CBE FBA.

Canvas. 72.7 by 61.7 cm.

Prov.: 12th Duke of Hamilton, Hamilton Palace, Lanarkshire, by 1882; Hamilton Palace sale, London (Christie's), 24th June 1882, lot 385; bought by G.J. Howard, later 9th Earl of Carlisle; thence by descent at Castle Howard until 1944; purchased in London by the present owner, 1952.

Lit.: MAHON 1968, pp.81-82, no.34; MAHON 1969, pp.66-67, no.43; SALERNO, p.132, no.55.

Although it was completed to represent a Sibyl with her traditional attributes of books and scrolls (see under cat.no.24 below), the painting was originally executed as a study for the figure of St Irene in the large *St Sebastian Succoured by St Irene* now in the Pinacoteca Nazionale Bologna (SALERNO, p.131, no.54; for the subject, see cat.no.3 above). Guercino subsequently altered the figure sufficiently for this painting to stand as an autonomous work, substituting the book and parchment for the sponge and bowl originally held by the saint, thus adapting a preliminary sketch – albeit a fairly finished one – into an independent painting he would have been able to sell.

The *St Sebastian Succoured* is one of the three pictures Malvasia (1678, II, p.364; 1841, II, p.259) records the twenty-eight-year-old Guercino painting in 1619 at Ferrara for Cardinal Jacopo Serra (whose patronage of Guercino is discussed under cat.no.9 below). The sketch, in its original form, can therefore be dated very accurately as it must have been made very shortly before the *St Sebastian Succoured.* A drawing for the whole composition by Guercino at Windsor (MAHON 1969, no.43; MAHON/TURNER, no.9) represents the almost finalised form of the composition at a late stage of its development. Two other, presumably slightly earlier, drawings at Florence (MAHON 1969, p.66, nos.41 and 42) show him experimenting with the composition in a vertical format. The figure to which the *Sibyl* corresponds appears only in the Windsor drawing.

That Guercino felt able to alter this sketch in order to produce a finished, saleable picture of another subject is indicative of the growing demand for his work even at this early stage of his career. Although it is naturally not one of his most important early works, this study is nevertheless a very fine example of his fluent handling and rich colouring, which, with the complex and dramatic play of light falling diagonally across the canvas, is highly typical of the works he produced before visiting Rome.

6. *Erminia and the Shepherd*

c.1619-20

Birmingham City Museums and Art Gallery (no.P17/62).

Canvas. 149 by 178 cm.

Prov.: Commissioned by Ferdinando Gonzaga, Duke of Mantua, in 1619 and recorded in the 1627 inventory of the Gonzaga pictures as no.236: '*Un quadro di mano de Guarcino da Cento dipintovi l'istoria del Tasso*'. It was not among the pictures sold from Mantua to King Charles I of Britain in 1627-28, and, according to an oral communication from Martin P. Eidelberg and Eliot W. Rowlands, does not appear in Gonzaga inventories of 1665, 1706 and 1709 (although this does not necessarily mean it had left the collection). Possibly in the collection of a 'M. Louvois' in France in the early eighteenth century, but next certainly recorded in the Comte de Vaudreuil sale, Paris (J.P.B. Lebrun), 26th November 1787, lot 2; François de Laborde de Méréville sale, Paris (J.P.B. Lebrun), 10th August 1803, lot 22. Reappeared in England, 1961, after which acquired by Birmingham in 1962.

Lit.: MALVASIA 1678, II, p.363f. (1841, II, p.259); A. BERTOLOTTI: *Artisti in relazione coi Gonzaga, Signori di Mantova*, Bologna [1885], pp.59-60; A. LUZIO: *La Galleria dei Gonzaga*, Mantua [1913], p.106; MAHON 1947, pp.70-71, note 113; R.W. LEE: 'Erminia in Minneapolis', in *Studies in Criticism and Aesthetics, Essays in honor of Samuel Holt Monk*, Minneapolis [1967], pp.36-57; MAHON 1968, pp.48-49 and 75-76, no.37; SALERNO, pp.140-41, no.61; MAHON 1991.

The picture was described by Malvasia as showing '*quando Erminia giunse da quel Pastore che tessea fiscelle, levato dal Poema del Tasso*' (Erminia encountering the shepherd weaving baskets, taken from the Poem by Tasso). It illustrates a passage from the beginning of the seventh canto of Torquato Tasso's epic poem *Gerusalemme Liberata* (VII: 8-13), in which the Saracen princess Erminia, who has disguised herself in armour to search for her lover the Crusading knight Tancred, retreats from battle, lays aside her armour, and encounters an old shepherd. This episode, symbolising the notion of a pastoral interlude amid the cares of life, was popular in the visual arts, and Guercino returned to it in 1648-49 when he painted two versions of the story (SALERNO, p.328, no.256; the other is lost). It is characteristic of Guercino's early works that he chose to represent a 'transitory' moment during Erminia's conversation with the shepherd, showing the latter pointing out of the picture space to the three boys who help him guard his flock. In the later composition the boys are depicted, not left to the imagination of the viewer, in a more spacious scene with a carefully balanced composition, slower narrative, idealised forms, and light subordinated to the forms rather than allowed an independent life of its own as in the present picture.

Although Malvasia's text misleadingly permitted it to be inferred that Guercino delivered this picture to the Duke of Mantua in 1618, it is clear from a letter written by the artist to the Duke on 17th September 1619 (published in Bertolotti) that the subject and dimensions had not yet been decided. This provides a definite *terminus post quem* for the canvas. The commission came about after a booklet of engravings – entitled *Esemplari per il Disegno* – by Oliviero Gatti after drawings by Guercino of anatomical details for the instruction of beginners in art had been dedicated to the Duke in 1619. Lorenzo Gennari, who had taken the presentation copy to Mantua, returned with a request to Guercino from the Duke for a painting '*a suo capriccio*' (of Guercino's own choosing). Guercino had many other commissions on hand at this time, and we have reasons for assuming that he did not start work on the picture before late in 1619; accordingly, it cannot have been completed before 1620. Guercino delivered it to the Duke in person, and, according to Malvasia, spent fifteen days at Mantua,

receiving 200 *scudi* for the work which pleased the Duke sufficiently for him to bestow a knighthood on the painter.

This picture is one of Guercino's most successful works of this period, combining a direct, almost ingenuous, presentation of the story with a number of superb passages of natural observation painted with intense feeling and a masterly touch. This everyday 'naturalism' with an intimate rustic flavour is indigenous to Guercino's artistic sensibility, and is not at all dependent on the example of Caravaggio.

For another painting by Guercino of a subject from Tasso, see cat.no.30 below.

7. *Head of Old Man*

c.1619-20

Lent by Sir Denis Mahon CBE FBA.

Canvas. 63 by 48.3 cm. On the back are the seals (for customs purposes) of the Habsburg-Lorraine Grand Duchy of Tuscany and the Papal Academy of Fine Arts, Bologna.

Prov.: Lt.-Col. R.W. Barclay, Dorking; acquired by the present owner in 1950. The seals give no clue as to earlier owners. Another version in the Hermitage, Leningrad, formerly catalogued as by Ribera, was published by Longhi as autograph, but has every appearance of being a copy.

Lit.: G. BRIGANTI: 'The Mahon Collection of Seicento Paintings', *Connoisseur*, no.132 [August 1953], pp.9, 13, 17; MAHON 1968, pp.87-88, no.38; R. LONGHI in *Paragone*, no.225 [November 1968], p.66, pls.52 and 53; SALERNO, p.142, no.62; MAHON 1991.

As Briganti pointed out in 1953, this is likely to be an oil-study from the life. There are several pictures by Guercino of about 1619-20 which include old men's heads painted with a very similar broken touch – including the shepherd in *Erminia and the Shepherd* (cat.no.6 above) and the *Elijah* (cat.no.9 below). It is not improbable that Guercino made oil-studies directly from models to use for guidance and adaptation when working on larger commissioned pictures, and he would probably not have found it difficult to sell this kind of study as a head of an apostle.

The probable date of around 1619-20 suggested by Mahon (1968) – rather than one in the period just after the artist's return to Cento from Rome in 1623 as was previously supposed by Briganti – is strengthened by evidence that has come to light regarding the change in Guercino's handling which began towards the end of his stay in Rome. It now appears that the looseness of touch evident here had by then already given way to a firmer and more solid handling in this type of subject.

8. *Jacob blessing the sons of Joseph*

1620

Lent by Sir Denis Mahon CBE FBA.

Canvas. 170 by 211.5 cm., possibly slightly cut down.

Prov.: Cardinal Jacopo Serra, Ferrara, 1620. After Serra's death in 1623 it presumably remained at Ferrara, and passed into the hands of Cardinal Giulio Sacchetti who succeeded him as Legate there less than fours years later. In 1646 Sacchetti is reported as having given it to the hereditary Almirante de Castilla, Don Juan Alfonso Enríquez de Cabrera, Duque de Medina de Rioseco, Spanish envoy to Pope Innocent X. Recorded in Cabrera's postmortem inventory drawn up in Spain in 1647; recorded in 1776 in the church of San Pascual, Madrid, which Cabrera's son had founded in 1683. Removed from the church by Don Manuel Godoy, Príncipe de la Paz in c.1803, and inventoried in his collection on 1st January 1808, but after the minister's downfall and the confiscation of his property in March 1808, it does not figure in an inventory of 1813; it might have passed between 1808 and 1812 to England, where a picture of this subject by Guercino was sold in 1813. It was recorded in the collection of Lord Northwick by 1843; sold by him in 1859 (with a provenance from T.S. Cave), it was rediscovered in 1932 in Paris, where the present owner acquired it in 1934.

Lit.: MALVASIA 1678, II, p.364 (1841, II, p.259); H. VOSS in *Zeitschrift für Kunstgeschichte*, II [1933], p.198; W. STECHOW: 'Jacob blessing the Sons of Joseph from Early Christian Times to Rembrandt'. *Gazette des Beaux-Arts*, New York ed., 6th series, XXIII [1943], pp.203ff.; MAHON 1947, pp.68f. and 72f.; MAHON 1968, p.93ff., no.42; I.J. ROSE WAGNER DE VIEJO: *Manuel Godoy, Patrón de las Artes y Coleccionista*, doctoral dissertation, Universidad Complutense de Madrid, 1983, Vol.II, no.264; SALERNO, p.145, no.66; MAHON 1991.

According to Malvasia, the picture was painted for Cardinal Serra in Ferrara in 1620, together with the *Elijah* (see cat.no.9 below). The subject is taken from Genesis XLVIII:1-22, recording how, when Joseph brought his sons Manasseh and Ephraim to their aged grandfather to be blessed, Jacob unexpectedly gave the right-handed blessing usually reserved for the firstborn to the younger Ephraim. Guercino shows Joseph protesting against this, and the composition is a particularly striking example of the artist's concern, around 1620, with the seizure of a fleeting but significant instant. As Wolfgang Stechow pointed out in his study of the picture's subject matter and symbolic meaning, the most 'transitory' and dramatic moment of the story has been selected; and indeed, as Mahon (1947 and 1968) has observed, this type of treatment is indeed completely antithetical to the type of 'classic-idealism' which Guercino was to encounter after his arrival in Rome the following spring. Nevertheless there can be no doubt that this picture and the *Elijah* were well received by Cardinal Serra, who conferred a knighthood on the artist in December 1620.

Three preparatory drawings for the composition have survived and it is significant that Guercino appears to have originally considered it in the reverse sense.

REG.III
CAP.XVI

9. *Elijah fed by Ravens*

1620

National Gallery, London (on long-term loan from Sir Denis Mahon CBE FBA).

Canvas. 195 by 156.5 cm. Inscribed on the stone slab: 'REG.III/ CAP.XVII'.

Prov.: Cardinal Jacopo Serra, Ferrara, 1620; mentioned in Barberini inventories from 1655 onwards; upon the division of the Barberini entailed estate in 1812 it passed to the Principi di Palestrina branch of the family, with whom it remained until purchased by the present owner in 1936; placed on loan to the National Gallery since 1987.

Lit.: MALVASIA 1678, II, p.384 (1841, II, p.259); H. VOSS in THIEME-BECKER: *Allgemeines Lexikon der Bildenden Künstler*, Vol.XV, Leipzig [1922], p.217; MAHON 1968, pp.91-93, no.41; SALERNO, p.147, no.68; MAHON 1991.

According to Malvasia, this picture was painted by Guercino for Cardinal Jacopo Serra in Ferrara in 1620, along with the *Jacob blessing the Sons of Joseph* (cat.no.8). The inscription refers to I Kings XVII:6, which describes how, after Elijah had prophesied a drought, God told him to hide himself by the brook Cherith, from which he could drink, and where ravens would feed him, bringing him 'bread and flesh in the morning and bread and flesh in the evening'. This is the most frequently portrayed of the several miraculous events in the life of the Old Testament Prophet; but it is interesting to note that, though Guercino has provided chapter and verse as to the biblical source on the tablet in front of Elijah, the picture appears to have been considered, in various seventeenth- and eighteenth-century Barberini inventories, to show the Christian saint, Paul the Hermit. (St Paul, who lived in Egypt during the third century AD, similarly received sustenance from ravens.)

Malvasia records five pictures painted by Guercino for Cardinal Jacopo (Giacomo) Serra. Serra was born in 1570 and was created a Cardinal in 1611. He was the Papal Legate of Ferrara (and hence Papal Governor of the territory to which Guercino's native town of Cento belonged) from 1615 until his death in 1623. Three were commissioned in 1619 (see under cat.no.5, above), when the young artist worked for him in Ferrara for some months, and Serra also visited Cento for a couple of days on 8th September 1619, when the city presented him with a painting by Guercino. Malvasia's account of the works Guercino painted in 1620 informs us that the artist 'was recalled to Ferrara where he made other pictures for the same legate, and for his nephew who delighted in drawings; and they were a picture of the prophet Elijah in the desert; Jacob blessing his son, all the figures the size of life'. Serra's enthusiastic admiration for Guercino is underlined by the fact that he conferred a knighthood on the artist in that year. The Cardinal also seems to have given Guercino a relatively free hand in choosing his subjects: those of the paintings destined for Serra are notably diverse.

In Guercino's compositions of around 1619-20, he tends to give massiveness to his forms by bringing them forward towards the spectator, allowing them to fill a high proportion of the picture surface, even touching the edges. At the same time, he alleviates this massiveness by breaking up the forms, and introducing unexpected juxtapositions and overlappings of the figures, assisted by effects of light which cut across them. It is particularly instructive here, in a picture which required only a single figure, to see how Guercino managed to retain a subtle balance between solidity and dissolution. The figure is given a disjointed centrifugal pose, and the impression that the prophet has been 'captured' in a fleeting movement is enhanced by the lighting, as well as by such effects as the shadow cast by an imagined object beyond the picture space on the slab of stone at the right. Although this is a relatively early work, Guercino's mature genius here finds its full expression.

10. *The Incredulity of St Thomas*

1621

National Gallery, London (no.3216).

Canvas. 115.3 by 142.2 cm.

Prov.: These are certainly the pair of pictures Malvasia (1678, II. p.361; 1841, II, p.260) speaks of as having been painted for Bartolomeo Fabri of Cento in 1621 (although he mistakenly calls no.11 '*Un Christo avanti a Anna*', i.e. Christ before Ananias; both compositions were engraved by Pasqualini in 1621, and the print of no.11 is dedicated to Fabri); the pair is recorded, also by Malvasia (1678, I, p.127; 1841, I, p.104), in the collection of Cardinal Ginetti, Rome, 1678; possibly in the Aldobrandini collection in the late eighteenth century; acquired by Thomas Hope of Deepdeene, Surrey, before 1818, perhaps when Hope was in Rome in 1792 (Hope lent them to the British Institution Exhibition of 1818 as from the Aldobrandini collection); sold at the Hope Heirlooms sale, London (Christie's), 20th July 1917, lots 96 and 95 respectively, when no.10 was bought by the National Gallery, and no.11 by R. Langton Douglas who presented it to the Fitzwilliam Museum in 1924.

Lit.: MALVASIA 1678, II, p.361 and I, p.127 (1841, II, p.260 and I, p.104); MAHON 1968, pp.103-06, nos.47 and 48; J.W. GOODISON and G.H. ROBERTSON: *Fitzwilliam Museum Cambridge. Catalogue of Paintings. Italian Schools*, Cambridge [1967], p.76; M. LEVEY: *National Gallery Catalogues. The Seventeenth and Eighteenth Century Italian Schools*, London [1971], pp.143-44; SALERNO, pp.153-54, nos.73 and 74; BAGNI, *Incisori*, pp.29-30.

11. *The Taking of Christ*

1621

Lent by the Syndics of the Fitzwilliam Museum, Cambridge (no.1131).

Canvas. 115.6 by 142.5 cm.

This pair of pendant pictures depict events immediately preceding and following the Passion of Christ. The *Taking of Christ* is described in all four Gospels, and Guercino, following a long tradition of representing the subject, has shown the moment when the group of menacing soldiers moves in to arrest Christ immediately after Judas has betrayed Him to them. The centrally placed Christ stands serenely with his hands clasped, gazing calmly at Judas who clutches the bag containing the thirty pieces of silver he had been paid for his treachery. The story of St Thomas's incredulity is described only in the Gospel of St John (XX:19-20). Thomas having been absent when Christ first appeared to the Apostles after His Resurrection, doubted that they had seen him: 'Except I shall see in his hands the print of the nails, and put my finger into the print of the nails, and thrust my hand into his side, I will not believe'. Guercino, portrays the moment, eight days later, when Thomas was bidden to do this. The

Apostle's face is shown, significantly in the dark, directed with intense concentration toward the wound Christ has invited him to touch. Christ, illuminated from beyond the picture space with his arms spread to allow the action and holding the white flag which traditionally symbolises the resurrection, looks down benevolently.

Malvasia mentions the paintings as having been made in 1621 for Bartolomeo Fabri, a fellow citizen of Cento and an early patron of the artist; they are therefore likely to have been completed before Guercino left for Rome in May of that year. While the composition of the *Incredulity of St Thomas* appears to have been entirely of Guercino's own invention, that of the *Taking of Christ* is closely related to a painting of the same subject by Ludovico Carracci (of which several versions are now extant, the principal one being in the Princeton University Art Museum), down to such details as the opened lantern that illuminates Christ and the rope which suggests a halo round His head. Guercino was much influenced by the work of Ludovico – who had died in 1619 – having studied, in particular, the altar-piece Ludovico had painted in 1591 for the Capuchin church at Cento.

Both paintings are striking examples of the horizontal compositions with half-length figures that Guercino frequently made, another being the *Christ and the Woman taken in Adultery* (cat.no.12 below). They are also notable for their dramatic narrative depiction of scenes of confrontation, in this case religious. Guercino was concerned with this sort of narrative – both secular and religious – throughout his career (for example, cat.nos.14 and 30).

12. *Christ and the Woman taken in Adultery*

c.1621

By permission of the Governors of Dulwich Picture Gallery.

Canvas. 98.2 by 122.7 cm.

Prov.: First recorded in Palazzo Mari, Genoa, 1766; imported into England 1806, and purchased by Sir Francis Bourgeois by whom it was bequeathed to the Gallery in 1811.

Lit.: P. MURRAY: *The Dulwich Picture Gallery*, London [1980], p.85; *Collection for a King, Old Master Paintings from the Dulwich Picture Gallery*, exh.cat., National Gallery of Art, Washington, and Los Angeles County Museum of Art [1985-86], pp.66-67, no.12 (entry by Mahon); SALERNO, p.155, no.75.

The episode of Christ and the woman taken in adultery occurs in John VIII:2-11. While Christ was teaching in the Temple the Pharisees brought to Him a woman who had been found committing adultery. When Christ was asked His opinion on the punishment, which under Mosaic law as written in the Torah, entailed stoning to death, He replied: 'He that is without sin among you, let him cast the first stone'. Guercino shows the moment when Christ is being questioned, and before He speaks.

Murray, Mahon and Salerno are in agreement that the picture dates from 1621, that is either shortly before, or immediately after, Guercino's arrival in Rome in May of that year. It may be compared to two pictures executed in 1621, just before his departure for Rome, the *Incredulity of St Thomas* and the *Taking of Christ* (cat.nos.10 and 11 above), both horizontal compositions with half-length figures, a type probably derived from the Venetian tradition, and one to which Guercino returned frequently during his career. They exemplify, as here, the artist's ability to convey the significance of a fleeting moment – notably, in the exhibited painting, through the arrangement of the hands.

For a double-sided sheet in the Albertina, Vienna, with preparatory drawings for the composition, see MAHON in the Washington/Los Angeles catalogue, cited above, p.66.

13. *St Chrysogonus in Glory*

1622

Not exhibited. Lancaster House, London. (Photograph courtesy *Country Life*).

Canvas. 500 by 295 cm.

Prov.: Painted for the ceiling of the church of S. Crisogono, Rome where it remained until it was acquired in Rome before 1808 by Alexander Day, at which time it was replaced in the church by a copy; Day attempted to sell it in London (Christie's) as '*The Apotheosis of St Paul*', though nevertheless from 'S. Grisogano [*sic*] in Rome' on 21st June 1833, lot 36; but it was bought in. Acquired shortly thereafter by the 2nd Duke of Sutherland, who placed it on a ceiling in Stafford House (renamed Lancaster House after it passed into national possession in 1911), St James's, London, where it remains.

Lit.: MALVASIA 1678, II, p.365 (1841, II, p.260); CALVI 1808, pp.19-20 and 163, note 26 (1841, p.287); G. WAAGEN: *Works of Art and Artists in England*, London [1838], II, p.248; MAHON 1947, p.80, note 131 and pl.20; MAHON 1968, p.6, note 12 and pp.110 and 112; MAHON 1969, pp.92-93, no.86; SALERNO, p.169, no.86; MAHON/TURNER, p.11, no.20.

St Chrysogonus was a Christian martyr of the early fourth century, about whose life remarkably little is known. He is believed to have been a priest who was arrested and imprisoned on account of his faith, and after various travels to have been beheaded at Aquilea in c.304 AD. His cult enjoyed some popularity in Rome in the fifth century, by which time the church of S. Crisogono was in existence in Trastevere, built on the spot where the saint's head was reputedly buried. In 1620 Cardinal Scipione Borghese initiated a remodelling of the church, which was completed by 1626. Guercino was probably asked to paint the ceiling decoration early in 1622, and is known to have received three payments from Borghese funds for work on it, on 25th June, 31st August and 2nd October 1622.

This large canvas, which is of course meant to be seen from below, shows the saint in glory, with no iconographical attributes or particular events from his life. He is borne up by a group of five putti, one of whom holds a palm branch to signify that he is a martyr. Chrysogonus himself gazes upwards past two angels playing wind instruments.

Guercino painted several ceiling decorations, particularly in the early part of his career, the most notable being the famous *Aurora*, painted for Cardinal Ludovico Ludovisi – whose family had been early patrons of Guercino in Bologna – in 1621 at the cardinal's villa at Rome (see the biographical introduction above). This was accompanied, also in 1621, by other ceiling decorations at Palazzo Patrizi (now Costaguti) and Palazzo Lancellotti. The commission for the church of S. Crisogono must have come from Cardinal Scipione Borghese soon afterwards.

The spatial complexity of the lower part of the painting, which is typical of Guercino's early work, with the putti darting in and out of the clouds and heavy emphases of light and shadow, contrasts with the considerably clearer and more evenly lit upper part and musical angels towards which the saint is moving. Indeed, he appears to be leaving the terrestial confusion below for the celestial clarity above. It was during Guercino's two-year sojourn in Rome that certain changes in his style began to occur, and the difference between the lower and upper halves of this large canvas show how subtly he began to integrate these changes into his art.

14. *The Presentation of Jesus in the Temple*

1623

National Gallery, London (on long-term loan from the Mahon Trust)

Copper. 72.5 by 65 cm.

Prov.: Painted for Bartolomeo Fabri of Cento, who later returned it to Guercino in settlement of a debt; sold by the artist to Raphael Trichet Dufresne, 1660; passed from the collection of the Abbé François de Camps to that of the Duc d'Orléans by 1727; acquired by the Earl Gower as part of his share of the Orléans collection in the 1790s; sold at London (Peter Coxe, Burrell & Foster), 13th May 1802, lot 63, when purchased by the 2nd Earl of Ashburnham; remained in the Ashburnham collection until acquired by Mahon in 1953; placed on long-term loan to the National Gallery by the Mahon Trust, 1977.

Lit.: MALVASIA 1678, II, p.366 (1841, II, pp.260f.); CALVI 1808, p.153 (1841, p.341); MAHON 1947, pp.93ff.; MAHON 1968, pp.135-37, no.53; SALERNO, p.178, no.94; MAHON 1991.

The episode of the presentation of the infant Christ in the Temple by Mary and Joseph is described in Luke II:22-35. The infant Jesus was brought to the Temple to be consecrated to the Lord as a firstborn son, a ceremony at which two turtledoves, shown by Guercino at the foot of the altar, were to be sacrificed. It had been revealed to Simeon, the high priest, that he would not die until he had seen the Messiah. Guercino has chosen to depict the moment at which Joseph takes the Christ Child from Mary to give him into Simeon's arms, that is before the moment of revelation in which Simeon recognises the Messiah with the words: 'Now lettest thou thy servant depart in peace, For mine eyes have seen thy salvation'.

This exquisite painting has been one of Guercino's most celebrated works since within the artist's own lifetime, and was described by Malvasia as '*questo famosissimo rame*'. Its early history, which has emerged from a close critical analysis of Malvasia's text and Guercino's account books (see MAHON 1968, and MAHON 1991), underlines this. Guercino painted it for his important early patron in Cento, Bartolomeo Fabri, in 1623, that is shortly after the artist's return from Rome (for two pictures painted for Fabri in 1621, immediately before he went to Rome, see cat.nos.10 and 11 above). Fabri later returned it to Guercino at cost price in partial discharge of a debt; the artist hung it in his own bedroom from which many very eminent collectors tried to extract it, including Cardinal Antonio Barberini, Francesco I d'Este Duke of Modena, and Cardinal Prince Leopoldo de' Medici. Guercino eventually sold it to the Frenchman Raphael Dufresne, who gave the artist a flatteringly inscribed copy of his edition of Leonardo's *Trattato* in addition to paying him 100 doubloons on 22nd December 1660.

In Mahon's view, the composition, lit by an evenly distributed light revealing a hitherto undeveloped respect for the clear definition of the planes, represents an entirely new departure for the artist. It evidently reflects the attention he had paid at Rome to examples of 'classic' composition particularly those of Domenichino. Domenichino's fresco of the *Death of St Cecilia* in the church of S. Luigi dei Francesi there was certainly well known to Guercino, and the disposition of the figures in the *Presentation* is more nearly related to that in Domenichino's composition than to anything we can find in Guercino's own earlier works. Indeed, the woman kneeling on the right could be described as a kind of fusion of the two women in the same position in the *Death of St Cecilia*.

Other aspects of the *Presentation* also seem to betoken a new orientation. The detailed depiction of both the vestment of the priest and of the marble reliefs on the altar and dais can be paralleled in the work of Domenichino. The drapery of the Virgin, more deliberately studied than had been usual before, and carefully arranged so that the bulk of it emerges into the light, could betoken some interest in the Roman works of Annibale Carracci. Very striking is the new rôle played by the architecture. Instead of the disconnected architectural fragments often found in Guercino's pre-Roman paintings, there is a comprehensive, clearly organised, architectural setting. Though the atmosphere is clearer than before, the colours are nevertheless rich and succulent and the handling appears still relatively broad and free compared to the precision with which, for example, Domenichino and Albani painted on copper. What we have here is a successful compromise, with which Guercino must have been well satisfied, between his North Italian upbringing, with its Venetian undertones, and the classic point of view which he had encountered in Rome.

15. *St John the Baptist visited in Prison by Salome*

c.1624-26

Lent by Sir Denis Mahon CBE FBA.

Canvas. 81 by 97.5 cm.

Prov.: Probably Borghese Collection; Admiral Lord Radstock (1753-1825); acquired by the 3rd Marquess of Lansdowne for Bowood House by 1844; by descent at Bowood until 1930; acquired by present owner in 1964.

Lit.: *Art in Italy 1600-1700*, exh.cat., Institute of Fine Arts, Detroit [1965], no.99; MAHON 1968, pp.123-24, no.52; E. PANOFSKY: *Problems in Titian: Mostly Iconographic*, New York [1969], pp.43ff.; *England and the Seicento*, exh.cat., Agnews, London [1973], no.33 with a note by Mahon on the evidence for a probable Borghese provenance; SALERNO, p.189, no.107.

St John the Baptist's imprisonment is recounted in the Gospel of Saint Mark VI:14-22. He was cast into prison by Herod, whom he had reproached for having illegally married his sister-in-law, Herodias. Herodias, who wished to have John killed, persuaded her daughter Salome to ask Herod to have the prophet beheaded. There is no biblical authority to suggest that Salome ever visited John in prison, and the unusual subject of this picture was first identified by Erwin Panofsky, who noted that the tradition of Salome's love for John (a tradition exemplified by Oscar Wilde's play *Salome*) stretched back well beyond the seventeenth century. Salome's visit has overtones of a temptation subject, analogous to the visions of beautiful women that tempted St Anthony in the Wilderness. Guercino shows John turning his head away, as if to reject temptation.

Another version of this subject by Guercino has come to light only recently, which Salerno (p.144, no.65) dates to around 1620. He also suggests that it may be the picture described – not altogether accurately – in the Will, dated 28th July 1621, of a certain Scaruffi of Reggio Emilia as a '*San Giovanni Battista con Erodiade*' (Saint John the Baptist with Herodias) which had been given to him by the artist.

The exhibited picture would then appear to be a later replica by Guercino of Scaruffi's picture, as stylistically it cannot predate the artist's Roman experience because of its affinities with the *Burial of St Petronilla* altar-piece of 1623 now in the Pinacoteca Capitolina, Rome (see SALERNO, p.174, no.92).

This picture shows the monumentally sculptural and classicising features that characterise Guercino's post-Roman works beginning to become apparent, with perhaps something of the robustness that only developed as Guercino digested his Roman experience on his return to Cento. Mahon is quoted by Salerno (p.189) as suggesting that it probably dates from 1624-26, when Guercino was on more than one occasion documented in Reggio Emilia.

Around 1670 the collector Don Antonio Ruffo (see under cat.no.30 below) received, probably from Abram Bruegel, a note of pictures for sale which included one which could apply to this composition: '*Del Guercino di p.^{ma} maniera di 3 p.^{mi} S. Gio in prigione con una Donna che lo tenta*' (by Guercino [and] of his first manner, of three *palmi* in size, St John in prison with a woman who tempts him; see *Bollettino d'Arte*, X [1916], p.190). This description seems to hint at the love of Salome for St John suggested by the apochryphal legend.

16. *Venus, Mars, Cupid and Time*

c.1624-26

The National Trust, Dunham Massey, Altrincham (The Stamford Collection).

Canvas. 127 by 175 cm. (oval).

Prov.: Unrecorded before the eighteenth century (if the seventeenth-century Italian frame is the original, the eight-pointed stars might be an allusion to an owner's coat of arms). First described in the collection of the 4th Earl of Stamford at Dunham Massey, 1769; taken by the 7th Earl of Stamford to Enville, Stourbridge, Staffs, and passed with that house to Sir Henry Foley Grey, 7th Baronet, in 1905; sold London (Christie's), 27th February 1931, lot 113, when bought by the 10th Earl of Stamford, who returned it to Dunham Massey; passed to the National Trust with Dunham Massey on the death of the 10th Earl in 1976.

Lit.: ST J. GORE in *Apollo* [July 1978], pp.27, 29 and 31; SALERNO, p.191, no.109; MAHON 1991.

In the inventory of the 4th Earl of Stamford's collection of 1769, this painting was described as 'an oval Picture representing the different stages of human life. Guercin'. In fact the characters represented are Mars, the god of war, wearing armour and holding his sword, Father Time with his crutch and hourglass, Venus, goddess of love, and her son Cupid. The allegory draws on two motifs common in Italian painting. The first is the chastisement of Cupid for the mischief he makes by causing people to fall in love. Here it is Father Time who admonishes him, rather than Venus herself or Mars as is more usual. The second allusion is to the discovery of Venus's adulterous affair with Mars by her husband, Vulcan: Vulcan forged a net in which the guilty couple were trapped while making love. Here, by a witty conceit, it is Cupid who is caught in the net, prefiguring his mother's disgrace. A drawing by Guercino for the picture, now lost but known from an engraving, is also of oval format, implying that Guercino originally planned it as such.

The Dunham Massey picture was published as Guercino's original by Salerno, on being informed by Nicholas Turner that it was likely to be the original of many copies, a view which Mahon accepts. On stylistic grounds it clearly dates from after Guercino's departure from Rome, and Mahon agrees with Salerno in dating it to around 1624-26 (1991). The existence of the copies testifies to its popularity. Guercino returned to the subject in 1656 in a painting made for Count Ferdinand of Werdenberg, which is now untraced.

Guercino used an oval format on several occasions (see for example nos.19 and 20 below). Here he uses it to great advantage in the placing of Venus on the right and, especially, of Cupid on the left. These two figures with their lighter flesh tones cause the other two figures to be pressed back into the picture space, creating a sense of depth, though with none of the recessional devices he would have employed before 1621. Accordingly, while the subtle use of light does recall Guercino's pre-Roman work, the comparative simplicity in the arrangement of the figures confirms the dating of the painting to the years shortly after his return to Cento.

17. *St Gregory with Sts Ignatius Loyola and Francis Xavier*

c.1625-26

Lent by Sir Denis Mahon CBE FBA.

Canvas. 296 by 211 cm.

Prov.: Commissioned by the Ludovisi family, probably in 1625 when they decided to build the church of S. Ignazio in Rome, and probably destined for it or the Jesuit buildings which adjoined it; given in 1646 by Niccolò Ludovisi to the hereditary Almirante de Castilla, Don Juan Alfonso Enríquez de Cabrera, Duque de Medina de Rioseco, and Spanish envoy to Pope Innocent X; recorded in Cabrera's post mortem inventory, drawn up in Madrid in 1647; recorded in 1776 in the church of San Pascual, Madrid, which Cabrera's son had founded in 1683; it appears to have left the church by 1815, as it is not recorded in a guide book of that year. Next recorded in Paris in the Baron Mathieu de Faviers sale 11th April 1837, lot 18, when it was purchased by the 2nd Duke of Sutherland and hung at Stafford (now Lancaster) House (see cat.no.13 above); Duke of Sutherland sale, London (Christie's), 8th February 1908, when purchased by Sir George Faudel-Phillips for his collection at Balls Park, where it remained until bought by the present owner in 1941.

Lit.: MAHON 1947, pp.98-102; MAHON 1968, pp.148-151, no.60 (with full bibliographical particulars); MAHON 1969, pp.104-05, nos.101-02; SALERNO, pp.192-93, no.112; MAHON/TURNER, p.20, no.35; MAHON 1991.

St Gregory the Great was the first pope to take the name Gregory. During his reign, from 590 to 604 AD, he established himself as one of the greatest of statesmen popes and was responsible for sending a mission, led by St Augustine, to convert the English. He is regarded as one of the four Doctors of the Western Church: the book he holds on his lap is a traditional attribute of the Doctors, and the elaborate papal tiara held by the putto in the foreground signifies his papacy. The dove is the Holy Spirit inspiring Gregory's writings.

The presence of the two principal saints of the Jesuit order, St Ignatius Loyola at left and St Francis Xavier at right, in an altar-piece whose main figure is St Gregory the Great, is highly significant. When Alessandro Ludovisi was elected Pope in 1621, he took the name of Gregory XV, and it was during his papacy that St Ignatius – the founder of the Society of Jesus – and St Francis Xavier – one of the Society's most important early missionaries – were both canonised on the same day, 12th March 1622, this being the feast day of St Gregory the Great. It was Pope Gregory's nephews Ludovico and Niccolò Ludovisi who caused the church of S. Ignazio to be built in Rome in honour of the newly canonised saint, though work in fact began only in 1626, three years after the Pope's death. The altar-piece's subject is so closely related to these events that it must have been commissioned from Guercino around the time the church was begun, though unfortunately no documentation relating to the commission appears to have survived.

The Ludovisi were one of Bologna's most eminent families, and had been early patrons of Guercino, who had worked for them since 1617. It was indeed Alessandro Ludovisi who called Guercino to Rome, together with another important Bolognese artist, Domenichino, when he became Pope in 1621. Guercino left Cento on 12th May of that year, remaining in Rome until the death of the Pope in July 1623.

The inclusion of the two Spanish Jesuit saints in the St Gregory altar-piece, probably played a part in shaping its subsequent history. The Pope's nephew Niccolò, Prince of Piombino, who became head of the Ludovisi family after the death of his brother Cardinal Ludovico in 1632, had close Spanish connexions through two of his three wives, and it seems highly probable that he gave the painting to Juan Alfonso Enríquez de Cabrera who visited Rome in 1646 as a special Spanish envoy to the newly-elected Pope Innocent X, whose niece Niccolò had married as his third wife in 1644. Cabrera had been the Spanish Viceroy at Naples, and was a major collector of paintings, to whom Cardinal Sacchetti gave Guercino's painting of *Jacob blessing the sons of Joseph* in 1646 (see cat.no.8 above). Both the *Jacob* and the St Gregory altar-piece were recorded among Cabrera's possessions after his death at Madrid in 1647, and both eventually went to the church of San Pascual in Madrid which had been founded by Cabrera's son in 1683. Baron Mathieu de Favier, who acquired the picture from the church around 1809-12, held a high official position with the French occupying forces in Spain.

Like the previous three paintings this work shows clearly aspects of Guercino's art that developed after his Roman years. Being an altar-piece, however, the painting could not have been composed along the lines of a horizontal frieze of figures; instead Guercino places the

figure of the principal saint centrally. With his particularly sumptuous robe, and the brilliant yellowish white of the book, St Gregory appears not so much to be lit, but to emanate light, an impression strengthened by the other two flanking saints, dressed in black, who have the effect of placing him in strong relief. Guercino has cleverly constructed an angled vertical axis that runs from the dove, through the saint himself to the infant *putto* below. This reduces the risk of rigidity in the composition and enhances the dynamism of the figure group; nevertheless an impression of monumentality is given which cannot be paralleled in Guercino's pre-Roman work.

18. *Mars*

c.1628

The National Trust, Tatton Park, Knutsford, Cheshire (The Egerton Collection).

Canvas. 116 by 94 cm.

Prov.: Perhaps painted for Cardinal Bernardino Spada in 1628; in the Albani Collection, Rome, before 1801; acquired by William Young Ottley, who exhibited it for sale, as part of a group of pictures he had purchased in Rome during 1799-1800, in London in January 1801 as 'Guercino. A Warrior in Armour; said to be Scanderberg', and giving the provenance as Palazzo Albani. Ottley then offered it for sale twice at auction in London (Christie's 16th May 1801, lot 35; and 25th May 1811, lot 84), both times unsuccessfully. Acquired, possibly from Ottley who died in 1836, by Wilbraham Egerton before his death in 1856; by descent to the 4th Lord Egerton of Tatton, who bequeathed it, together with the house and its contents, to the National Trust in 1958.

Lit.: E. BOREA: *Pittori Bolognesi del Seicento nelle Gallerie di Firenze*, Florence [1975], p.200, under no.148; SALERNO, pp.216-17, no.123 bis; MAHON/TURNER, pp.85-87, under no.166; MAHON 1991.

Mars, the God of war (see also cat.nos.16 and 19) is shown in characteristically martial pose. When offered for sale in London in the early nineteenth century, the picture was described as a portrait of the Albanian national hero George Kastriota (1403-68), called by the Turks Iskander Bey, *viz.* 'Skanderbeg'. This is entirely fanciful, but it has enabled Mahon (1991) to trace the provenance to William Young Ottley, who stated that it had been acquired from Palazzo Albani, Rome.

Nicholas Turner first suggested that the style of the picture points to a date at the end of the 1620s, and it is not out of place in the vicinity of the *Martyrdom of St Lawrence* of 1628. There is, in fact, an indication that Guercino may have painted a *Mars* in that year for Cardinal Bernardino Spada, who was Legate of Bologna between 1627 and 1631, but this depends on the interpretation of source material among his papers (see MAHON 1991).

There is a good workshop copy of the picture in a private collection which bears the inscription 'SPIRANS MINARVM ET CAEDIS': the Latin is ungrammatical, but it probably means 'breathing forth threats and slaughter', a motto appropriate to Mars.

19. *Mars*

20. *Venus and Cupid*

1630

Wellington Museum, Apsley House, London; lent by courtesy of the Board of Trustees of the Victoria and Albert Museum.

Canvas. Each 113.7 by 84.2 (oval).

Prov.: Painted for Lorenzo Fioravanti of Bologna; a label with an inscription in French on the back of no.20 suggests that they were in France during the early nineteenth century; acquired by the 1st Duke of Wellington (1769-1852); by descent to the 7th Duke, who presented them to the nation with the Wellington Museum in 1947.

Lit.: MALVASIA 1678, II, p.367 (1841, II, p.261); CALVI 1808, pp.60f. (1841, p.308); C.M. KAUFFMANN: *Catalogue of Paintings in the Wellington Museum*, London [1982], p.67; SALERNO, pp.224-25, nos.130-31; MAHON/TURNER, p.30, no.55.

The amatory affair between Mars, the god of war, and Venus, the goddess of love and wife of Vulcan is one of the most enduring of the popular classical myths. Among the many ways in which artists represented them, paired images such as these became popular from the

fifteenth century onwards. Mars is shown brandishing his sword and gesturing, as if departing, presumably for some warlike activity. Venus, on the other hand appears to make a remonstrative gesture as her son Cupid points his bow out of the picture while drawing an arrow from his quiver. The arrow is evidently intended for Mars.

It can be inferred from Malvasia's unchecked, and so confusing, text (which gives rise to the erroneous implication that there were four paintings) that these two pictures were painted for '*Sig. Lorenzo Fioravanti Bolognese*' in 1630; and in fact payments for them are recorded in the *Libro dei Conti* on 23rd February, 17th March and 26th March of that year (see CALVI). These payments make clear that Guercino was at work on the paintings during that period. As with many of Guercino's less important works for patrons not of the first rank, their early history is not known.

Four years later, in 1634, Guercino painted a single painting incorporating all the three figures represented in these two oval canvases for the Duke of Modena (it is now in the Galleria Estense, Modena). It is, however, clear from the account book that these two exhibited paintings were always separate compositions, and they are likely to have been oval from the start (they were certainly oval when the French label on the rear of no.20 was written). In the single painting Mars is shown as less aggressive, holding a staff rather than a sword, while Venus points her finger and Cupid his already loaded bow at the viewer. These paintings exemplify the wit and charm Guercino could achieve, particularly in his more intimate compositions.

21. *St Agnes*

1637

Private collection; loan arranged by courtesy of Trafalgar Galleries, London.

Canvas. 119.5 by 94 cm.

Prov.: 1637, commissioned by Alberto Provenzali of Cento to give to Cardinal Girolamo Colonna; probably the painting of St Agnes in the sale of the property of the Earl of Shrewsbury, Alton Towers, 8th July 1857, lot 228; sold from the collection of Richard Corbet, Adderley Hall, Shropshire in London (Sotheby's), 7th July 1976, lot 37.

Lit.: MALVASIA 1678, II, p.371 (1841, II, p.264); CALVI 1808, pp.80-81 (1841, II, pp.315-16); *Catalogo dei Quadri . . . Casa Colonna in Roma*, Rome [1783], p.103, no.789; SALERNO, p.251, no.163; MAHON 1991.

One of the most celebrated Roman martyrs, St Agnes was executed for defending her virginity. Here she is shown with a martyr's palm and with a lamb, the latter having become her attribute on account of the similarity between her name and the Latin word *agnus* and because of the sacrificial nature of the animal. In fact, her name derives from the Greek word meaning 'chaste'.

From Malvasia and the *Libro dei Conti* (Guercino's account book; see CALVI) it can be deduced that this picture was commissioned in 1637 by Alberto Provenzali (or Provenzale) of Cento as a gift for Cardinal Girolamo Colonna, the Archbishop of Bologna. A deposit of 25 *scudi* was paid on 4th March 1637, and the balance of 40 *scudi* on 18th June 1637; this order of price for a large half-length of this size had become standard in Guercino's system of pricing (see under cat.no.24 below).

Denis Mahon has pointed out (orally) that Cardinal Colonna was at this time an admirer of Guido Reni as well as of Guercino, and that certain delicacies of handling and colour may be discerned in the *St Agnes* which suggest that Guercino was not altogether unmindful of this fact.

22. *The Penitent St Peter*

1639

National Galleries of Scotland, Edinburgh (no.39).

Canvas. 103.7 by 85.8 cm.

Prov.: In the Gerini collection, Florence by 1786 (as Guercino); acquired from the family in 1831 by the Royal Institution, Edinburgh; transferred to the National Gallery of Scotland, 1858.

Lit.: MALVASIA 1678, II, p.364 (1841, II, p.264); CALVI 1808, p.88 (1841, II, p.318); H. BRIGSTOCKE: *Italian and Spanish Paintings in the National Gallery of Scotland*, Edinburgh [1978], pp.60-61, no.39; SALERNO, p.264, no.179.

The story of St Peter's tearful repentance at having thrice denied Jesus on the evening of his arrest, is told in Mark XIV:29-31 and 66-72: 'And when he thought thereon, he wept'. The image of St Peter weeping became popular in the early seventeenth century as a devotional subject embodying the frailness of man's resolve and the need for repentance.

Mahon – whose arguments are reported by Brigstocke – has suggested that this picture is the '*S. Pietro piangente*' (St Peter weeping) described by Malvasia (1678, II, p.364; 1841, II, p.264) as having been painted for Cardinal Rocci in 1639. This work also appears in the *Libro dei Conti*, the account book kept on Guercino's behalf by his brother, which records the artist receiving 55 *scudi* – implying that the painting was likely to have been a lifesize half-length figure – on 4th April 1639 for '*il San Pietro fatto all' E.mo Sig. Cardinale Rocci Legato di Ferrara*' (the St Peter made for the most eminent Cardinal Rocci, Legate of Ferrara; see CALVI). Cardinal Ciriaco Rocci had been Vice-Legate under Cardinal Serra, that ardent early collector of Guercino's painting (see under cat.no.9 above), and he had probably inherited the Legate's enthusiasm for the artist. After he returned from Rome to Ferrara in 1637, he commissioned a picture of *Lucretia* from Guercino in 1638, and in the same year the city of Cento presented him with a *Lamentation* by the artist (now at Rennes, Musée des Beaux-Arts; see SALERNO, p.260, no.175).

A date of 1639 is perfectly plausible stylistically for this picture, which shares the robustness of some other works of this period. Furthermore, the identification of the Edinburgh picture as the one painted for Rocci in 1639 was greatly strengthened by Denis Mahon's discovery of a letter of 10th February 1639 (transcribed in MAHON 1968, p.148). In it, an unknown individual, called Fra Gioseffo, describes how he visited Guercino's studio, and reports to his unidentified addressee that the artist was 'also attending to painting a half-length Saint Peter that would be appropriate for you, and he is making it for the most eminent Rocci'. Fra Gioseffo goes on to say that he considered 'that it will be one of the [most] beautiful things one could believe in the field of painting, and if your illustrious self would like me to try to have a copy [made] by a good artist – indeed by a very good one – I will see what can be done to serve you, provided that permission is given for a copy to be made'.

From this it would appear that Guercino was too busy to take on a new commission, but the possibility that a copy may have been made makes the existence of a good workshop version of the Edinburgh picture in the Palazzo Venezia, Rome, of particular interest. It would seem that a copy was indeed made; the quality of the Palazzo Venezia version was such that in the eighteenth century – when it was in the collection of Cardinal Tommaso Ruffo – it was held to be an original by Guercino.

Guercino painted a *Penitent St Peter* again, in 1650 (SALERNO, p.339, no.269). After over ten years had elapsed, a change can naturally be seen in Guercino's style when comparing this with the Edinburgh picture.

23. *The Agony in the Garden*

c.1640-45

National Museum of Wales, Cardiff (no.A7).

Canvas. 221 by 155 cm.

Prov.: Probably still in the artist's house at his death; in the collection of the Earl of Burlington at Chiswick House by 1728 (see p.4 above); subsequently it passed with the Burlington Collection to the Dukes of Devonshire at Chatsworth, where it remained until 1976; purchased by the National Museum of Wales in 1978.

Lit.: MALVASIA 1678, II, p.384 (1841, II, p.273); *Italian Paintings 1550-1780*, exh.cat., P. & D. Colnaghi Ltd, London [1976], no.10; SALERNO, p.286, no.207; MAHON 1991.

Christ's agony in the Garden at Gethsemane is described in the Gospels of Matthew, Mark and Luke, but only Luke (XXII:39-46) mentions the appearance of an angel: 'And he was withdrawn from them for about a stone's cast, and kneeled down, and prayed, Saying, Father, if thou be willing, remove this cup from me: nevertheless not my will but thine, be done. And there appeared an angel unto him from heaven, strengthening him. And being in an agony he prayed more earnestly: and his sweat was as it were great drops of blood falling down to the ground.' Guercino has represented Christ contemplating the cup of sorrow (which, appropriately for a picture that may originally have been commissioned for an altar, resembles a communion chalice) and has depicted beads of sweat on His forehead as though they are blood. In this way, the Passion is foreshadowed as well as by the inclusion of the nails with which He will be crucified.

This picture is probably identical with the '*Christo grande orante nell'Orto con l'Angelo & Apostoli in lontananza*' (large [picture] of Christ praying in the garden with the angel and apostles in the distance) that Malvasia describes as having been amongst those that remained in Guercino's house at the time of his death. These dated from various moments in his career; Salerno places this picture in the early 1640s for stylistic reasons.

The single figure of Christ, lit clearly from above and kneeling firmly on the ground, is monumental in a way which is notably different from an earlier treatment of a single figure, the *Elijah* (see no.9 above). In this painting the blocks of colour are simply disposed, heightening the legibility of the composition. The gestures of Christ, from the chalice with one hand to the angel with the other, are continued by the angel's own gesture out of the picture space towards the divine source of the light, thus indicating the connexion of divine light with the Passion through Christ. The apostles sleeping in the background are deliberately subdued: while their presence is important for the narrative, Guercino has not allowed them to distract our attention from the figure of Christ.

24. *The Phrygian Sibyl with a Putto*

1647

Private collection, England.

Canvas. 114.6 by 96 cm. Inscribed on the tablet: 'SCINDETVR TEMPLI VELVM SIBYLLA PHRYGIA' (the veil of the temple shall be rent in twain; Phrygian Sibyl). A later, probably eighteenth-century, addition to the canvas in the form of a strip across the bottom, measuring 5.5 cm., has recently been removed.

Prov.: Painted for Marchese Girolamo Albergati, Bolognese Ambassador at Rome; in an English private collection since the nineteenth century.

Lit.: MALVASIA 1678, II, p.375 (1841, II, p.267); CALVI 1808, p.115 (1841, II, p.327); *Italian and the Italianate*, exh.cat. Hazlitt, Gooden & Fox, London [1990], pp.12-15, no.3, with full documentation supplied by Mahon; MAHON 1991.

The Phrygian Sibyl is one of the twelve Sibyls adopted by the Christian church as pagan counterparts to the Old Testament Prophets, it being believed that, like the prophets, they had foretold the coming of Christ. In pagan lore they had been the prophetesses of Apollo: each takes her name from the place of her origin and has a particular prophecy associated with her. The Phrygian Sibyl's prophecy was that 'Our Lord shall rise again'.

There is a long tradition of depicting the Sibyls in Italian painting, and from the fifteenth century they are most frequently shown with books or scrolls as their attributes, referring to the Sibylline Books in which their prophesies are recorded (although individual Sibyls may have individual attributes on occasion). They were particularly popular as the subjects of painting in the seventeenth century. Guercino frequently painted Sibyls, the earliest (though the subject was arrived at as an afterthought) being no.5 in this catalogue. After his visit to Rome he began to paint Sibyls more frequently, and in 1626-27 he painted a series of frescoes in Piacenza cathedral, which include eight of the twelve Sibyls. A *Cimmerian Sibyl* followed in 1638 (SALERNO, p.263, no.178), but it was later in his career that Guercino painted the greatest number of Sibyls, in the late 1640s and early 1650s (see also cat.nos.27, 28 and 31 below).

Guercino's account book records the receipt of 70 ducats from the Bolognese ambassador in Rome on 21st May 1647 (see CALVI) in payment for a *Phrygian Sibyl*. This is the only time this subject is described in the *Libro dei Conti*. A date in the later 1640s is wholly acceptable for this picture, which is identified as the Phrygian Sibyl by the prominent inscription. Malvasia also mentions that Guercino painted a *Phrygian Sibyl* in 1647, and identifies the Bolognese ambassador in Rome who ordered it as the Marchese Girolamo Albergati.

Guercino's system of pricing his works by the figure finds some corroboration in another half-length Sibyl painted by the artist in 1647, the *Persian Sibyl*, now in the Pinacoteca Capitolina, Rome (SALERNO, p.312, no.238, paid for in June). For this contemporary work, of identical dimensions, Guercino received 64 *scudi*, in contrast with the 87½ *scudi* charged for the *Phrygian Sibyl* (the sum of 70 ducats recorded in the *Libro dei Conti* for the *Phrygian Sibyl* being the equivalent of 87½ *scudi*). The difference in cost – of just over 23 *scudi* – between these two half lengths can be explained by the inclusion of a putto in the *Phrygian Sibyl*, for which Guercino would have charged extra.

The Marchese Girolamo Albergati is known to have disposed in Rome of pictures he had commissioned in Bologna, and it is likely that this picture passed to another collection at this time. A copy seems, however, to have remained in the Palazzo Albergati in Bologna where it was recorded in the 1770s by Marcello Oretti who attributed it to '*I Gennari*' (that is to say the Gennari family, Guercino's relations by marriage) which is tantamount to classifying it as a school picture.

Although only a half-length figure this Sibyl, like many larger paintings by Guercino, appears monumental. She amply fills the picture space, her severe profile adding to the seriousness of the subject: she pauses from her reading to peruse the inscription on the tablet supported by a suitably grave *putto*. However, the cool impression she conveys is rendered less chilling by the rich variety of colours in her dress. The prominent orange of the sleeve is especially striking, as is the beautifully rendered texture of the red velvet band across her breast.

SCINDETVR
TEMPLI
VELVM
SIBYLLA
PHRYGIA.

25. *St Cecilia*

1649

By permission of the Governors of Dulwich Picture Gallery.

Canvas. 119 by 98 cm.

Prov.: Probably the picture painted for the Marchesa Virginia Turca Bevilacqua in 1649; first definitely recorded in 1804, in the collection of Noel Desenfans; bequeathed by him to Sir Francis Bourgeois, by whom it was in turn bequeathed to the Dulwich Gallery in 1811.

Lit.: MALVASIA 1678, II, p.376 (1841, II, p.267); CALVI 1808, pp.120 and 123 (1841, pp.329-30); J.P. RICHTER: *A Descriptive and Historical Catalogue [of the Dulwich Picture Gallery]*, London [1880], pp.70-71, no.234; P. MURRAY: *The Dulwich Picture Gallery*, London [1980], p.300, no.237 of the list of unexhibited pictures, as by Gennari; SALERNO, p.336, no.266; MAHON 1991.

A Roman virgin martyr whose origins are somewhat unclear, St Cecilia is represented as the patron saint of music only from the fifteenth century onwards. Her association with music seems to depend on a sixth-century hagiography which describes how she heard heavenly music as she was led to the house of her betrothed, and asked God to keep her body and soul without stain.

This picture bore a traditional attribution to Guercino when in the collection of Noel Desenfans, but was arbitrarily attributed in Richter's Dulwich catalogue of 1880 to Benedetto Gennari, the leading figure in Guercino's workshop from the late 1650s onwards. Mahon identified the picture as an autograph work and shared his view with Salerno who published it as such. It bears no resemblance to the work of Benedetto Gennari.

Mahon suggested to Salerno that the picture could be identified as the half-length picture painted for the Marchesa Virginia Turca Bevilacqua in 1649. Guercino received an initial payment of 25 *scudi* for this on 30th September 1648, and the balance of 50 *scudi* on 4th January 1650 (see CALVI). Malvasia also records the picture under the year 1649 and describes the patron as Ferrarese. The dates of Guercino's other versions of this subject (1642, 1643, 1658 and 1659) cannot easily be reconciled with the style of this picture.

In fact this work must be close in date to the *Phrygian Sibyl* (see no.24), but the mood is perhaps closer to the *Libyan Sibyl* (see no.31) painted some two years later than the *St Cecilia*. The saint is very much engaged in her music-making, much as the Libyan Sibyl is involved in her reading, and the air of the painting is calm and intimate, entirely suited to the private home for which it was presumably commissioned.

26. *David with the Head of Goliath*

1650

Trafalgar Galleries, London.

Canvas. 120.5 by 102 cm.

Prov.: Painted for Lodovico Fermi of Piacenza; in the collection of Ranuccio II Farnese, Duke of Parma, c.1680, and subsequently inherited from the Farnese by the Bourbon Kings of the Two Sicilies at Naples; sold from the collection of John Udney, London (Christie's), 25th April 1800, lot 46, described as from 'the Parma collection'; bought by Colonel Murray; sold London (Sotheby's), 9th November 1927, lot 5; private collection in Copenhagen until 1982.

Lit.: MALVASIA 1678, II, p.378 (1841, II, p.269); CALVI 1808, pp.125-6 (1841, p.331); G. CAMPORI: *Raccolta di cataloghi ed inventari inediti*, Modena [1870], p.239; *Trafalgar Galleries at the Royal Academy III*, exh.cat. London [1983], no.6, pp.16-18; SALERNO, p.342, no.272; MAHON 1991.

The story of David and Goliath is told in I Samuel XVII:4-58 and XVIII:6-9. David swore to Goliath that the Lord would deliver him unto his hand, and that he would take Goliath's head from his shoulders. Having felled the giant with a stone from his sling, David, who had no sword, then used Goliath's own sword (here shown behind Goliath's head) to behead him. Guercino painted the subject on at least five occasions in his career.

This picture can be identified as the one mentioned by Malvasia for the year 1650 and recorded in the *Libro dei Conti* in the same year as: '*Mezza figura del Davide, con la testa di Golia gigante*' (Half-length figure of David, with the head of the giant Goliath; see CALVI), for which Guercino received 60 *ducatoni* (i.e. 75 *scudi*) from Lodovico Fermi of Piacenza. It must have passed fairly soon into the ducal collections at Parma, since it is described in the inventory of about 1680 of Farnese pictures in the Palazzo del Giardino there (see CAMPORI). None of the other extant versions of the subject or those described in the early sources conform with the price and the appearance of this picture, which also appears to fit stylistically into the artist's work of around 1650, the period in which he developed a greater refinement of touch and a rather paler colouring that may be compared with Guido Reni's later works. It is typical of the artist that he has invested a traditional subject with expressive elements that make a more profound examination than is often the case in pictures of the victorious David, of David's thanks to God for having slain his enemy.

27. *The Cumaean Sibyl with a Putto*

1651

Lent by Sir Denis Mahon CBE FBA.

Canvas. 222 by 168.5 cm. Inscribed 'O LIGNVM BEATVM IN QVO DEVS EXTENSVS EST SYBILLA CVMANA' (O blessed wood on which God was stretched out; Cumaean Sibyl).

Prov.: Painted in 1651 for Gioseffo Locatelli, but sold by the artist in May of that year to Prince Mattias de' Medici. It does not appear in any known Medici inventories. Acquired from an unknown source, probably between 1830 and 1840, by Sir John Forbes, 7th Baronet, for Fintray House near Aberdeen, and inherited by his great-grandson, the 19th Baron Sempill. When the house was demolished, the picture was sold, and was acquired by the present owner soon afterwards, in 1954.

Lit.: MALVASIA 1678, II, p.378 (1841, II, p.269); CALVI 1808, p.128 (1841, p.332); E.K. WATERHOUSE: *Italian Baroque Painting*, London [1962], p.166, Fig.99; MAHON 1968, pp.195-97, no.90; *England and the Seicento*, exh.cat., Agnews, London [1973], no.37; SALERNO, p.351, no.281; MAHON 1991.

The Cumaean Sibyl, who historically was Apollo's priestess at Delphi, was admitted into the Christian Sibylline canon (see under cat.24 above) for having predicted that Christ would be born of a virgin in a stable at Bethlehem, and the inscription refers to the wooden cross on which Christ would be crucified. There are several allusions to this Sibyl in classical literature, including Ovid's *Metamorphoses* and Vergil's *Aeneid*, and she seems to have been the most popular of the Sibyls to be represented in Italian painting.

Guercino was originally commissioned to paint this picture by Gioseffo Locatelli of Cesena as a companion for the *David* now in the Spencer collection at Althorp (see cat.no.29). However, as Malvasia records, it was seen in the artist's studio by Prince Mattias de' Medici, who admired it and made a special request to purchase it, paying 197 *ducatoni* (i.e. 237 *scudi*) on 26th May 1651 (see CALVI). Guercino was then obliged to paint another Sibyl for Locatelli as a companion to the *David*, the *Samian Sibyl* (cat.no.28), also at Althorp. This explains why the Althorp picture and the present *Cumaean Sibyl* are so similar in style and composition and virtually identical in size. It is, however, a testament to Guercino's originality and honesty that he did not in these circumstances merely produce two identical versions of the same composition.

The monumental figure fills the centre of the composition and, although the range of colours is limited, Guercino has achieved an astonishing effect of richness by placing the pink sleeve of the Sibyl's right arm in the very centre of the picture. All the other colours – a variety of blues, browns and greys – appear to revolve around this bright colour. The whites of the open books, the Sibyl's turban and cuffs provide sufficient accents in the painting to prevent the large stone areas from becoming bland. This kind of masterly economic handling of colour can be found in many of Guercino's important later paintings (see nos.28, 29, 30, 32).

O LIGNVM
BEATVM IN
QVO DEVS
EXTENSVS
EST
SYBILLA
CVMANA

28. *The Samian Sibyl with a Putto*

1651

Canvas. 218.5 by 180 cm. Inscribed on the scroll held by the putto: 'SALVE CASTA SYON PER MVLTAQVE PASSA PVELLA' and 'SYBILLA SAMIA' (Hail, chaste Sion who has undergone much suffering; Samian Sibyl).

29. *King David*

1651

Canvas. 223.5 by 167.5 cm. Inscribed on the tablet: 'GLORIOSA DICTA SVNT DE TE CIVITAS DEI. PSALM 86' (Glorious things are spoken of thee, O City of God).

Not exhibited. Reproduced by kind permission of the Earl Spencer, Althorp House, Northampton.

Prov.: Both painted for Gioseffo Locatelli of Cesena, 1651. Purchased from the Locatelli heirs at Cesena for the 1st Earl Spencer by Gavin Hamilton, 1768; by descent to the present Earl Spencer.

Lit.: MALVASIA 1678, II, pp.378-79 (1841, II, p.269); CALVI 1808, pp.128, 129 (1841, p.332); W. MARSH: 'Iconography of the Sibyls', in F.C. HUSENBETH: *Emblems of the Saints*, Norwich [1882], Appendix I, p.406; O. PIERACCINI in *La piè*, no.4 [July-August 1975], pp.151-54; SALERNO, pp.352-53, nos.282-83.

Of the twelve Sibyls (see under cat.no.24 above) the Samian was said to have prophesied that Christ would be born of a virgin. King David's rôle as a prophet is clear in the Old

Testament, and indeed the fact that he was King of the Jews was taken to prefigure the coming of Christ: this is clearly set down in the Gospel according to Matthew, which begins by claiming David (and before him Abraham) as a direct ancestor of Christ. It is therefore appropriate that a painting of David should be paired with one of a Sibyl in Christian art, on account of their prophetic rôles. In fact this association of David with a Sibyl (though not with a specific Sibyl can be found in a thirteenth-century hymn used in the roman *Missa pro defunctis* or Mass for the dead: '*Dies irae, dies illa,/Solvet saeclum in favilla:/Teste David cum Sibylla*' ('The day of wrath, the dreadful day,/Shall sweep this age in flames away: So David and the Sibyl say'; see HUSENBETH). The two are further linked in these paintings by the references to Sion, the City of God, in the inscriptions.

These two pendant paintings of David and a Sibyl, were commissioned from Guercino by Gioseffo Locatelli of Cesena in 1651. However, the *Samian Sibyl* is not in fact the painting that was originally destined for the patron: Guercino had painted a *Cumaean Sibyl* as a companion to the David, but, as is explained under cat.no.27 above, a special request to purchase it was made on a visit to the master's studio by Prince Mattias de' Medici, who paid for it on 26th May 1651. Guercino was therefore able to deliver only the *David* to Locatelli, who paid him for it on 16th May 1651. The second *Sibyl* which Guercino, changing the subject to a Samian Sibyl, painted to replace the one bought by the prince, was delivered to Locatelli later in the year and paid for on 7th October.

Both the *David* and the *Samian Sibyl* have a serenely calm atmosphere, and Guercino has characterised both figures with an impressive intelligence: David, the author of the psalms contemplates the inscription from Psalm 86 on the tablet he supports ('Glorious things are spoken of thee, O city of God'; now actually Psalm 87, verse 3), and the Sibyl reads with quiet concentration. Guercino's composition and handling are entirely appropriate to these contemplative subjects, just as his dramatic treatment in cat.no.30 below is to the subject of Erminia and Tancred.

30. *Erminia finding the Wounded Tancred*

1651

Not exhibited. Reproduced by kind permission of Castle Howard, Yorkshire.

Canvas. 244 by 287 cm.

Prov.: Commissioned, possibly towards the end of 1649, by Cardinal Savelli, Papal Legate of Bologna, but probably not begun until 1650; purchased from the artist by the Duke and Archduchess of Mantua, who saw it in the artist's studio in 1651 and paid for it on 6th May 1652; in the collection of the Comte de Lauragais, Paris, by 1772; sold London (Christie's), 27th February 1772, lot 70 (as *Angelica and Medora* [*sic*]), when purchased for the 5th Earl of Carlisle for £525; thence by descent at Castle Howard.

Lit.: MALVASIA 1678, II, p.376 (1841, II, p.267); MAHON 1968, pp.191-94, no.88 (with documentation regarding the change of patronage and subsequent history); *England and the Seicento*, exh.cat., Agnews, London [1973], no.36; SALERNO, p.355, no.285; G. JACKSON STOPS, ed.: *Treasure Houses of Great Britain*, exh.cat., National Gallery of Art, Washington [1985], pp.348-49, no.275.

The episode of *Erminia finding Tancred wounded* is taken from canto XIX, lines 103-114, of Tasso's epic poem *Gerusalemme Liberata* (see also cat.no.6 above), in which the poet describes how the crusading hero was wounded by the Egyptian Argantes during the Crusaders' onslaught on Jerusalem. His loyal armour-bearer, Vafrino, shown at the right in the painting, fetched Erminia, who arrived stricken with grief at the plight of her lover. She then bound his wounds with her own hair, to which Guercino has given prominence in his portrayal of her.

Erminia finding the Wounded Tancred is one of the most frequently depicted episodes from Tasso in seventeenth-century Italian painting, along with *Erminia and the Shepherd*. Guercino had treated both subjects early in his career: his *Tancred wounded* of 1618-19 is today in the Galleria Doria-Pamphili in Rome (SALERNO, p.130, no.53) while his *Erminia and the Shepherd* of 1619-20 is no.6 in the present exhibition.

As Malvasia records, Guercino in fact made the present picture as a pair to an *Erminia and the shepherd*, now in the Minneapolis Institute of Arts (SALERNO, p.328, no.256), which he had painted some two years earlier in 1649. The vicissitudes of the commission (see MAHON 1968) are not without interest. The *Erminia and the Shepherd* was to have been for the Sicilian collector, Antonio Ruffo, but it was seen in 1649 in Guercino's studio by Cardinal Savelli who successfully persuaded Guercino to allow him to take it, producing another rendering for Ruffo. Guercino then painted the pendant *Erminia finding the Wounded Tancred*, for Savelli himself. Unfortunately for Savelli, history repeated itself: his picture was seen by the Duke and Archduchess of Mantua, who, even though it was not yet finished, desired it. Savelli allowed them to have it, and Guercino received payment from the Duke on 6th May 1652.

The painting now at Castle Howard is one of Guercino's most prestigious pictures of the early 1650s. A comparison between his early treatment of the subject of 1618-19 (in the Doria Pamphili collection, as noted above) shows the great change that had taken place in Guercino's painting over a period of some thirty years. The earlier work is highly complex, with the figures placed tightly within the composition and deliberately entwined in a subtly conceived group. The flickering light and rich, dark colours often (and purposely) make it difficult to distinguish individual figures from each other. In the later painting, this complexity has given way to a clarity and simplicity in the spatial organisation. Each figure occupies a well-defined area, the central recumbent figure of Tancred being flanked by the more animated figures of Erminia and Vafrino. The frieze-like nature of the composition is further emphasised by the indistinct treatment of the middle-ground and the theatrical backdrop of the distant landscape. It is this evenness and balance that has led to Guercino's later paintings being termed 'classical'. This does not imply, however, that their dramatic impact is any less telling. The great success of Guercino's treatments of such moments of drama between lovers such as *Samson and Delilah* or *Venus and Adonis* remained one of the artist's great strengths throughout his career.

SYBILLA LIBIA.

31. *The Libyan Sibyl*

1651

Not exhibited. Reproduced by Gracious permission of Her Majesty The Queen.

Canvas. 115.6 by 94.6 cm. Inscribed on the book under the Sibyl's elbow: 'SYBILLA LIBIA'.

Prov.: Probably one of the half-length paintings of Sibyls (Samian and Libyan) for which Ippolito Cattanio of Bologna paid 120 *ducatoni* on 4th December 1651. Purchased for George III by the Royal Librarian, Richard Dalton, probably shortly after 1760 in Italy; it has subsequently remained in the Royal Collection, at Buckingham Palace, Windsor, Hampton Court, and since 1980 at Buckingham Palace again.

Lit.: MALVASIA 1678, II, p.379 (1841, II, p.269); CALVI 1808, p.130 (1841, p.333); M. LEVEY: *The Later Italian Pictures in the Collection of Her Majesty The Queen*, Oxford [1964], p.84, no.521; MAHON 1968, pp.197-98, no.91; SALERNO, p.356, no.286.

Of the twelve Sibyls (see under cat.no.24 above) the Libyan Sibyl was distinguished for having prophesied the manifestation of Christ to the gentiles. Her usual attribute is a lighted torch or taper, possibly a reference to the words of the *Nunc Dimittis* spoken by Simeon at the presentation of Christ in the Temple (see under cat.no.14 above) which refer to Christ as 'a light to lighten the gentiles'. Guercino has chosen not to include this; the standard attribute of prophets in general is books, and the only means of identifying this Sibyl is the inscription on the closed volume.

Like the *Phrygian Sibyl* (see cat.no.24), which was painted slightly earlier than this picture, this is one of many half-length treatments of similar subjects by Guercino. However, this painting differs greatly in mood from the *Phrygian Sibyl* (as indeed it does from the two larger, contemporary paintings of Sibyls that are nos.27 and 28 of this catalogue) in being more lyrical and poetic. The alert attitude of her predecessor in 1647 is here replaced with an air of quiet concentration. There is no putto to disturb her and the light falls evenly over her, causing a subtle shadow on the right of her face. Yet just as rich colour saves the *Phrygian Sibyl* from being too severe, the serenity of the *Libyan Sibyl* is countered by the slightly frivolous bow at her waist.

32. *The angel appears to Hagar and Ishmael*

1652-53

Lent by Sir Denis Mahon CBE FBA.

Canvas. 193 by 229 cm.

Prov.: Commissioned by Pandolfo Saccini of Siena; in the collection of Adriano Salimbene at Siena by 1714; acquired from that family in 1751 by the 2nd Marquess of Rockingham, on whose death in 1782 it was inherited by his sister, Lady Anne Watson-Wentworth, wife of the 3rd Earl Fitzwilliam, from whose descendants it was acquired by the present owner in 1948.

Lit.: MALVASIA 1678, II, p.379 (1841, II, p.269); CALVI 1808, p.134 (1841, p.334); G. BRIGANTI: 'The Mahon Collection of Seicento Paintings', *Connoisseur*, no.132 [August 1953], pp.10-11, 14, 18; MAHON 1968, pp.201-203, no.94 (with many bibliographical references); SALERNO, pp.366-7, no.299; MAHON 1991.

The story of Hagar and Ishmael is told in Genesis XVI:1-16, and XXI:1-21. Hagar was the Egyptian servant of Sara, Abraham's wife. Being old and childless, Sara gave Hagar to Abraham as a concubine so that he might have a child. Some years later Sara miraculously gave birth to Isaac and asked Abraham to banish Hagar and her son Ishmael so that they would not rival Isaac as Abraham's heir. (Abraham's expulsion of them was painted by Guercino on another occasion; see Fig.10 on p.9 above). In the present picture, Guercino shows them in the Wilderness, represented as a pleasant wooded landscape, to which they had been expelled with only a little bread and water. According to the Biblical account, these supplies ran out and Hagar placed the child under 'shrubs' (which Guercino has interpreted as a tree) and sat down a 'bowshot' away, turning her back so as not to see her son die. As she sat weeping an angel appeared telling her to pick up her child and predicting that he would be the progenitor of a great nation (the Ishmaelites). At this point her eyes were opened and she saw a source of water, which Guercino includes at the extreme left. Guercino – who often sought out the psychological story in traditional narratives – is plainly more interested in this picture in Hagar's agony than in Ishmael.

Malvasia describes the picture as having been painted in 1652 for a Sienese patron and the *Libro dei Conti* records payment of the equivalent of 240 ducats from Pandolfo Saccini from Siena on 17th March 1653 (see CALVI; in the 1808 edition the name is misread or misprinted as Paccini, an error repeated in the 1841 edition).

As in the *Agony in the Garden* (cat.no.23 above) Guercino has emphasised the principal figure by placing her in the centre of the composition, illuminating her clearly and brightly from above. The figure of Ishmael to the right is far more subdued, as is the landscape background. These last serve to remind us of the narrative, like the apostles in the *Agony in the Garden*, but they are not allowed to distract our attention from Hagar. The warm colours of her drapery are deliberately contrasted with the cool blue of the angel above, as he indicates the water.

Briganti has described this picture as among the most poetic works of Guercino's late, classic style and emphasises its importance for English artistic circles of the second half of the eighteenth century; the passage is quoted in full by Mahon (1968).

Bibliographical Abbreviations

BAGNI, *Incisori*. Prisco Bagni: *Guercino e i suoi incisori*, Rome [1988].

CALVI 1808. Jacopo Alessandro Calvi: *Notizie della vita e delle opere del Cavalier Giovan Francesco Barbieri detto il Guercino da Cento*, Bologna [1808] (in which is published Guercino's *Libro dei Conti* or Account Book, on pp.58-160).

CALVI 1841. See under MALVASIA 1841.

MAHON 1947. Denis Mahon: *Studies in Seicento Art and Theory*, London [1947].

MAHON 1968. Denis Mahon: *Il Guercino. Catalogo critico dei Dipinti*, exh.cat., Bologna [1968]. Facsimile reprint, Bologna [1991].

MAHON 1969. Denis Mahon: *Il Guercino. Catalogo critico dei Disegni*, exh.cat., Bologna [1969].

MAHON 1991. This refers to the forthcoming catalogue by Denis Mahon, to be published by Nuova Alfa Editoriale of Bologna, of the exhibition which will be held at Bologna and Cento from September 1991. An English-language edition, accompanying a smaller exhibition, will be published by the National Gallery of Art, Washington D.C., in March 1992.

MAHON/TURNER. Denis Mahon and Nicholas Turner: *The drawings of Guercino in the collection of Her Majesty The Queen at Windsor Castle*, Cambridge [1989].

MALVASIA 1678. Carlo Cesare Malvasia: *Felsina Pittrice, Vite de Pittori Bolognesi*, Bologna [1678]. (The life of Guercino is in Vol.II, pp.358-86).

MALVASIA 1841. Carlo Cesare Malvasia, *Felsina Pittrici, Vite de' Pittori Bolognesi*, 2nd edition, Bologna [1841] Vol.II, pp.255-74 (in which is also published Guercino's Account Book, Vol.II, pp.307-43, reprinting CALVI 1808).

SALERNO. Luigi Salerno: *I Dipinti del Guercino*, Rome [1988].